Unity Church of Peace
905 E. Colfax Ave.
South Bend, IN 46617

COMPULSIVE OVEREATERS GUIDE

By PEARL BRIANS

Leader of weight groups

BRIANS PUBLISHING COMPANY

PENNGROVE, CALIFORNIA

1968

PRINTED BY HOOPER PRINTING & LITHOGRAPH CO., SAN FRANCISCO

DEDICATION

This book is dedicated to GRACE, a wonderful person in my life who helped me to have a living faith in a Higher Power, so I could lose 20 pounds and start on my road to recovery from compulsive overeating.

Special Thanks to my husband

Bert

For all his loving care and work in
helping me prepare this book. Thanks
to him for putting up with my compulsive
personality.

DISCLAIMER STATEMENT

The author is not a professional, doctor, psychologist, dietician or counselor, but she has the ability to write this book because of her extensive experience in leading weight groups and helping overweight persons for many years. She has helped many frustrated women and girls to a happier and healthier life. She tells about the feelings, emotions, and experiences of the compulsive overeater whom she assisted. These are her findings and personal opinions.

She does not knowingly advocate any brand names or groups without permission.

ACKNOWLEDGMENTS

This book contains thoughts and helpful hints saved during the author's many years of leading weight control groups. All kinds of inspirational self-improvement books, literature, and people have helped her write this book of positive thoughts and information to help the compulsive overeater who still suffers. Ideas and quotations have been taken from a number of sources, some of whom wish to remain anonymous. Names and credit are given to those who wish to be acknowledged. If any quotes are given without permission, it is only coincidental.

TABLE OF CONTENTS

We are so accustomed to negative thoughts that we need to have positive ones repeated over and over again so they will replace the negative ones. Repeated reading of this book will enable the compulsive overeater to give up fattening foods willingly in order to lose weight and KEEP IT OFF.

Preface

This book is written for all compulsive overeaters. It is hoped that its contents will give hope and strength to thousands who suffer from this terrible compulsion for food.

Compulsive overeaters are usually frustrated, unhappy and resentful because they don't have the will power to lose weight and keep it off. There are also many who are only five or ten pounds overweight. It is not the amount of weight that makes us unhappy but our attitude toward it.

Some people say they are a "happy fat". For them this book will do no good. It is written especially for the person who realizes that it isn't just because he likes food that he is overweight. He realizes that the obsession to eat compulsively is only the outer manifestation of his inner emotional conflicts. The food and fat are not our problems; our problems are our problems. We are our own worst enemy. In this book I hope to show many, if they will be open minded, a new way of arresting this disease of the mind and body called "compulsive overeating".

If you feel you are a normal eater then don't read this book. You won't believe it and you might even laugh at its contents. Only the person who is desperate in his search for a solution to overcome his compulsion can be helped. If he really wants to quit bingeing and obtain normal eating habits, he can succeed just by following the ideas in this book. In my opinion the only way to recovery is to give up all man-made sweets and starches entirely until your normal goal is reached. Then, and only then, should you attempt to eat like a normal eater. Even after you reach your goal you might find that you still cannot control your desire to want too much of them.

This is a sign that you need spiritual and emotional help by a therapy of some kind. Of course there are mental health clinics but many do not include spiritual help. Ask your Chamber of Commerce about such groups or start your own Self-Improvement Club. Groups for recovery from any compulsion are usually started by someone in deep need to effect a change in his life. There are many clubs for compulsive overeaters but be sure they will help you. Some people fight certain kinds of therapy and get worse. This book is helpful only if the person who needs to lose weight will read parts of it at least once a day or more. The more compulsive he is about foods the more he needs to read it; over and over again until he has convinced himself into believing the STEPS FOR RECOVERY.

1

AUTHOR'S NOTES

I feel that I am qualified to write this book not because I was obese but because I was a compulsive overeater. Since I was twelve years old I've been dieting intermittently. At that time my dad said, "You are going to be fat like Mama, and there's nothing you can do about it!" I became disturbed by his accusation and in my mind set up the thought, "I'll show him—I don't have to be fat!"

From then on I began to read books on diet and health. I started exercising and eating healthful foods to prove to myself and others that I was not going to be fat. God gave me the courage and determination to keep fighting my overweight problem. I did have times of giving in to foods and gaining weight, but I never became obese.

In 1962, I was twenty pounds overweight and miserable. My husband and children would tease me. Other people would ask me, "Are you pregnant?" My stomach and hips had all my extra weight. These are the two reasons I didn't give up. So people challenged me to keep trying to get my body trim and attractive.

Later, my husband read an article in the local newspaper about a club for compulsive overeaters. I went to meetings weekly but I resisted the STEPS FOR RECOVERY. "Eat only three meals a day," they said, "nothing in between meals except black coffee, tea, or water." No one was going to tell me not to snack in between meals! I knew how to diet! I was very stubborn. I found out later that I had to let go absolutely for a physical, mental and spiritual growth. I wanted to lose weight but did not give up my snacks of carrots or protein tablets in between meals. I felt guilty, but lost ten pounds at that. The other ten pounds were harder to lose because I kept fighting the spiritual side of the program which was presented. "Turn your will over to God," they would say at the meetings, "He won't let you eat too much."

At that time I didn't have much faith that God could help me. I had gone to church all my life, but I didn't have a living faith. I felt that if God was like my earthly father, He wasn't very loving and couldn't care or help me. I knew in my heart that this wasn't true, but now after years of study and therapy with leading weight groups, I realize that it is only natural for a person to relate to God as he does his earthly father. Now looking back, it seems that most of my emotional life stemmed from my poor relationship with not only my father but my mother as well.

I've learned that children need to be loved for what they are and not what they do, or do not do. I began to forgive both of my parents for lack of love and understanding because I realized they too were probably not secure in their own lives. My dad was very dominant and my mother gave me the feeling that men were not to be trusted. She gave me the impression that sex was dirty and that it was just a necessary evil.

As a child, I felt unworthy for being alive because my mother let me know that she had wanted me to be a boy. I hope none of you parents make this terrible mistake by telling your child he was not wanted in any way. I was a very bashful child. I had crossed eyes and felt ashamed of my glasses. I didn't have many friends at school because I felt insecure. I know now that anyone can have friends if only he can be one.

I was over-protected and loved by my mother and was not disciplined properly for self-esteem. My father, to my recollection, never showed me any kind of love, either spiritual or physical. We were a large family who had a poor income. My dad spoke of us girls as a nuisance and would remind us, "I'll be glad when you get married off, so I won't have to support you." He would tell all of us children, "You will never amount to a hill of beans."

I am happy to report that later in my adult life I did have the chance to find out that my father was not such a cruel man as I had visualized. During his later years after my mother died, he broke his hip and had to recuperate with someone to care for him. None of the rest of his six children would accept the responsibility, so I reluctantly did. This was a turning point in my life because when my father moved into a room which we had prepared for him, he actually cried out of gratitude. I was grateful to God for giving me the chance to know my father as a real person with feelings.

The reason I have gone into the details of my past is so that some parents who happen to read this book might be helped and not make the same mistakes. Since I've read many self-improvement books telling how our adult lives are affected by childhood experiences, I am not surprised at my frustrations in later life, which led to compulsive eating.

If a child experiences disapproval more than love and acceptance, it may result in him becoming a dope addict, drunk, or he may bite his nails, have headaches, arthritis, constipation, diarreah, acne, allergies, and many other physical symptoms. Wouldn't it be wonderful if our grammar schools could deal with the subject of "Self-acceptance" for the insecure child? Teachers and others who relate to the emotionally disturbed child can do wonders in helping him to accept his life and parents without resentments. The need to fight for his rights as a person would no longer be a struggle if he could look at his problems rationally instead of emotionally.

Looking back on my childhood after making so much progress in getting rid of inferiority, guilt, hate and fears, I realize that if I had received counselling from a mature adult, I could have been saved many heartaches. I recently passed a writer's school test which helped me to have the initiative to use my talent for writing this book. Also another therapy group has revealed to me that I have a great capacity to give love to unhappy persons. Now whenever someone criticizes other people for their particular shortcomings, I try to understand the reasons people act the way they do.

As I continued my search for a cure from overeating, I began to accept myself, because I knew that in order to love others, I must love myself first. The Bible tells us, *"Love Thy Neighbor as Thyself."* I used to wonder what that meant. Now I realize that only as we understand and love ourselves and others can we learn to love and understand God. God relates Himself through people. I've arrested the disease of "compulsive overeating", for I believe that it is a disease of the mind, body, and spirit, and that a thorough analysis of these three facets of life can bring complete recovery to the sufferer.

I used to criticize all fat people, but now I automatically love them and wish that I could share my knowledge of overeating with them. I expect this book to help hundreds of frustrated people to a healthier and happier life. It not only can help compulsive over-eaters, but can also help any neurotic person with a physical symptom caused from misunderstanding himself.

TEST

How Compulsive are YOU?

So you think that you are a compulsive overeater. Well, here is a test you can take which will tell you just how compulsive you really are:

1. Do you dislike yourself in many areas?
2. Do you feel some relatives or other people disapprove of you?
3. Have you dieted for any period of time, but failed to stay on it for any lasting length of time?
4. Do you think you overeat just because you like food?
5. Do you eat in front of others like a so-called "normal eater", but come home and sneak food or eat in other private places?
6. Do you turn to sweets or starches more than any other kind of food when you are hungry?
7. Do you avoid weighing on the scale or do you weigh more than once a week?
8. Do you feel the need for a snack after meals or between meals?
9. Have you ever been to a doctor about your weight?
10. Do you hate to look in the mirror at your nude body?
11. Do you eat when upset, angry, fearful, or because of self-pity, resentment, boredom, feeling of guilt, rejection, or inferiority?
12. Do you dislike the way you look in your clothes?
13. Have you felt still hungry even after you've eaten a moderate meal?
14. Does your weight make you or others unhappy?
15. Do you repeatedly try to lose weight without turning to God or a Higher Power?
16. Do you avoid public places because of your size?
17. Have you been unable to stop after 1 piece of candy, 1 piece of pie or cake, 1 piece of bread, 1 cookie, 1 dish of ice cream, 1 pastry

or 1 helping of potatoes, or 1 helping of any other sweets or starches?

18. Do you eat between meals?

19. Do you hate yourself or feel guilty or upset after overeating?

20. Do you think about food too much? Do you look at recipes and pictures of food often and plan ahead with joy to when and what you will eat?

21. Do you eat leftovers from other peoples plates or when cleaning off the table or doing the dishes?

22. Do you have difficulty staying on a diet very long?

23. Do you resent others who try to help you lose weight?

24. Do you think you overeat for emotional reasons?

25. Has your doctor told you to lose weight?

26. Do you feel ashamed of having to ask for help?

If you answer "yes" to more than five of these questions, you are probably a compulsive overeater and need help. You cannot do it alone. There is help and lots of it if you are willing to be open-minded and follow the suggestions in this book. Read parts of it over and over again in order to brainwash yourself into changing not only your compulsive eating habits, but your whole personality as well.

TWELVE STEP RECOVERY
FOR COMPULSIVE OVEREATERS
(Anonymous)

1. I admit that my life is unbearable and the obsession for food has made my life unmanageable.
2. I will come to believe in a Power greater than myself so that I can be restored to normal living.
3. I will make a decision to turn my will and my eating and whole life over to the care of God as *I understand Him.*
4. I will make a searching and fearless inventory of myself, by going back into the past.
5. I will admit to God, to myself and to another person the exact things I have done wrong.
6. I am entirely ready to have God remove all my bad eating habits and other defects of character.
7. I will humbly ask Him to remove all of my shortcomings, such as guilt, hate, fear, resentments, and inferiority feelings.
8. I will make a list of all relatives and people that I have hurt and I will be willing to make amends to all of them.
9. I will make direct amends to all of these persons wherever possible, unless it would hurt them or others worse than it would me.
10. I will continue to take my personal inventory every day and when I am wrong, I'll promptly admit it.
11. I will have a devotional life of prayer, reading, meditation, and thought each day so that I can improve my conscious contact with God, as I understand Him, seeking knowledge for His will in my life, and the courage to carry it out.
12. After I've had the spiritual awakening as a result of taking these steps, I will try to carry this message to all compulsive overeaters who will listen. I'll practice these principles in all my affairs.

WHAT ARE REFINED CARBOHYDRATES?

Here is a list of foods which should be given up ENTIRELY at least until your desired weight goal is reached. Then and only then should you trust your compulsive personality to eat a small amount, because these are the "binge" foods of a compulsive overeater.

FOODS TO AVOID

For the compulsive overeater

(All refined carbohydrates; man-made sweets and starches)

SUGAR (any kind)

CANDY (all kinds)

JAM, MARMALADE, JELLY

SYRUPS

PIES, CAKES, COOKIES, ALL PASTRIES

REGULAR SOFT DRINKS

REGULAR GUM AND CANDY COATED GUM (25 calories per stick)

NOODLES, SPAGHETTI, (any kind of macaroni product or foods containing these starches)

ALCOHOLIC BEVERAGES (Including beer, wine and any others)

ALL KINDS OF DESSERTS CONTAINING SUGAR

ANY FOODS CONTAINING THE ABOVE STARCHES (or flour)

BREADS (all kinds, even diet)

CEREALS (hot or cold)

ICE CREAM

GRAVIES, WHITE SAUCE, POPCORN, POTATO CHIPS, PRETZELS, CRACKERS, OR ANY BREAD PRODUCT.

If it contains any sugar or starch—don't eat it!

NEVER EAT BETWEEN MEALS!

This might seem to the compulsive eater that he has to practically quit eating, but let us look at the positive side of a no carbohydrate food plan. In the first place, almost all your "binge" foods are in the above categories. So if you are determined and open-minded enough to give these harmful foods up completely, you will have a steady weight loss. You have so many more healthful and yes, even tasty foods to enjoy and help you to be the happier slim person you wish to become.

FOODS TO EAT
(counting calories and carbohydrate grams)

PROTEIN (all kinds)

EGGS (scrambled, deviled, omelet, fried, boiled, coddled, baked, or any other way)

MEATS (any lean beef, lamb, deer, pork, or any other kind)

POULTRY (chicken, turkey, duck or any other kind)

FISH (all kinds, even tuna)

NUTS (count calories)

FATS (some polyunsaturated margarine + oil; 2 - 3 T daily)

MILK PRODUCTS (skim milk; cottage cheese, any kind; cheese, in moderation; buttermilk)

VEGETABLES (eat large amounts of these *except* corn, potatoes, peas, lentils, dry beans, and others high in natural carbohydrates) green beans, spinach, swiss chard, beets, carrots, lettuce, tomatoes, cauliflower, broccoli, cabbage, cucumbers, greens, onions, parsley, dill pickles (not sweet), peppers, saurkraut, tomato juice, asparagus, artichokes, celery, mushrooms, eggplant, squash.

FRUITS (all kinds of raw ones in moderation counting calories and carbohydrate grams; apples, applesauce (unsweetened), apricots (dry or fresh), banana, cantaloupe, cherries, figs, grapefruit, grapes, lemons, oranges, nectarines, peaches, pears, persimmons, pineapple, plums, prunes, raisins, dates, watermelon, berries (all kinds unsweetened). *All fruits should be eaten raw whenever possible. Wash juice off of all canned fruits.)*

JUICES (all kinds of fruit or vegetable not containing sugar or starch)

SOUPS (all kinds not containing refined carbohydrates (sugar or starch), bouillon, consomme; any clear soup)

OTHER LIQUIDS (vinegar, diet drinks, plain tea, coffee in moderation, water is the *best*.

IF YOU ARE IN DOUBT ABOUT WHAT IS GOOD TO EAT ASK THIS: Did God make it or did man make it? Man-made foods are usually harmful foods to all compulsive overeaters because they cannot eat these foods in moderation. God planned all the good foods aplenty.

HAPPY HEALTHY EATING!

So, you see, the most healthful and best foods are really the only ones you need and should want. In fact, if you care about the health of your family you will see that everyone stays on this healthful way of life. How much you love yourself and them depends on how you feed yourself and others. We need to reeducate ourselves about what foods are really "good". Old habits can vanish for better ones. Some people will say, "I need some starches and sweets." But I reply, "You have enough fat on your body to supply you for a long time and the wheat germ you can eat daily will take the place of all minerals and vitamins found in bread." For quick energy in place of sugar, you can eat a few dried dates, prunes or figs, or a teaspoon of honey. Now your excuses for eating sweets and starches are all gone, so stop fighting if you want to lose weight. Many people find after the withdrawal pains and desires for these foods for a period of six weeks, they no longer "crave" them. Why not be open-minded and give it a try? You have nothing to "gain" (fat) and everything to "lose" (fat).

Some members of clubs have gone so far as to say to their families, "I am sick. I crave these foods. If you must have them, please go down to the store and buy them and eat them, so I won't have to be tempted." This sounds like a drastic measure, but sometimes a person is so compulsive that only drastic steps can control him. It is up to the love and cooperation of each family to decide how much each member in the family is willing to cooperate. If it is hard to remember what foods are refined carbohydrates, remember this: All the natural foods are the healthful ones. These foods are given to us by God. All the refined carbohydrates or fattening foods are made by man. We can remember them easier that way. I'm hoping and expecting this book to bring the American people a healthier, happier, and longer life.

JUST FOR TODAY

Read this every day, preferably in the morning

JUST FOR TODAY, I will try to live through this day only, and not tackle my whole life problem at once. I can do something (diet) for twelve hours that would appall me if I felt I had to keep it up for a lifetime.

JUST FOR TODAY, I will be happy. This assumes to be true what Abraham Lincoln said, "Most folks are as happy as they make up their minds to be."

JUST FOR TODAY, I will adjust myself to what is, and not try to adjust everything to my own desires. I will take my "luck" as it comes, and fit myself to it.

JUST FOR TODAY, I will try to strengthen my mind, I will study. I will learn something useful. I will not be a mental loafer. I will read something that requires effort, thought and concentration.

JUST FOR TODAY, I will exercise my soul in three ways, I will do somebody a good turn, and not get found out; if anybody knows of it, it will not count. I will do at least two things I don't want to do—just for exercise. I will not show anyone that my feelings are hurt; they may be hurt, but today I will not show it.

JUST FOR TODAY, I will be agreeable. I will look as well as I can, dress becomingly, talk low, act courteously, criticize not one bit, not find fault with anything, and not try to improve or regulate anybody except myself.

JUST FOR TODAY, I will have a program. I may not follow it exactly, but I will have it. I will save myself from two pests, hurry and indecision.

JUST FOR TODAY, I will have a quiet half hour all by myself, and relax. During this half hour, sometime, I will try to get a better perspective of my life.

JUST FOR TODAY, I will be unafraid. Especially I will not be afraid to enjoy what is beautiful, and to believe that as I give to the world, so the world will give to me.   (*Anonymous*)

Note: This should be read often until it is all accepted.

MOST COMPULSIVE OVEREATERS ARE NEUROTIC

The title might upset some readers who will deny the statement. But the ones who admit it are more likely to get help than the ones who disbelieve it.

We must remove our guilt feelings about overeating because it is our inferiority feelings that cause our compulsions for food. Many neurotics have the capacity to become great people. What we need is to understand ourselves realistically instead of emotionally. A lot of frustrations are caused by lack of knowledge.

We don't understand ourselves so we feel no one else understands us. This is probably true. If all mankind could try to find out why others act the way they do instead of criticizing what they do, this world would be a much happier place in which to live.

A prescription for sleeping tablets or nerve pills has never solved anyone's problems. Troubles are only repressed for a time. Sooner or later they come back. Neurotic overeaters must face up to themselves the way they really are and then be willing to get some kind of help. A moral inventory should be taken. Spiritual guidance and growth are necessary. Therapy and discussion with others help tremendously.

Look back into history and you can think of many famous people who were neurotic. Some neurotics are successful and some fail. Successful ones are happy and unsuccessful ones are miserable. Famous neurotics no longer get criticized by society, but those who try something different and fail get blamed by the world for their eccentric actions.

Individualists must have their self-respect and be accepted for what they are, not for what they appear to be or what others want them to be. Disapproval is another reason why misunderstood people search for solace in food.

Physical symptoms such as compulsive talking, eating, smoking, drinking, nail biting, thumb sucking and many others are only a sign of lack of love and understanding. No one really wants to have any of these habits. We overeaters say, "We just like food, we just feel like eating, foods taste so good." Obese people do not want to be fat. They just don't have the right outlets.

Physical symptoms are usually a sign of an emotional conflict within and our bodies are crying out for help by gaining weight.

Many troubles start in childhood because of some situation over which a child had no control. A death, fire, accident, divorce, fight, poverty, and many other traumatic experiences in childhood can be a cause of compulsive overeating in later life. We as children tend to repress shocking or unhappy experiences instead of taking them in our stride.

Sometimes we become neurotic over trivial things someone said, such as, "You're too fat, too skinny, ugly, lazy, no good, bad, etc. . . ." Just one little remark from one person can hit a sensitive child and bring ruin to his life because he feels rejected or disapproval from others.

When a normal person says, "Grow up!" to the nervous, childish person, it only puts more burden and guilt on him. What he needs is understanding and love so he can mature properly.

The neurotic who succeeds is far happier than the normal person who has no particular goals in life and lives a routine existence. Neurotics have an uneasy feeling about life and themselves. This is only a sign that we are qualified for better things and we haven't found our true selves yet. We must respect ourselves and understand why we feel as we do. We must stop being afraid or ashamed of ourselves. We have to get to know ourselves; then we can get the strength and courage to do something about it. Then a truly wonderful person will emerge from the old self.

Some overeaters are book-worms. They go into private places and read. This is good if it is channeled in reading constructive literature. We are often too sensitive, too sentimental, too conscientious and pressed with indecision.

Compulsive overeaters are usually so sensitive they cannot act like normal people. They cannot enjoy a light conversation, but feel the need to talk of more meaningful things. Their lives are vital and very meaningful; they need only to channel this wonderful exuberance into something creative. Neurotics should be happy they are different from the ordinary person because they have hidden talents that can come to the surface and bloom into something great. Our discord and despair can sometimes spur us on to bigger and better things. Most people admire anyone who is daring enough to be himself even if he is different from others.

Sometimes parents stunt their children's emotional growth by trying to make them do exactly as society suggests. Schools are getting more knowledge and understanding of the need for individual growth of the child. The world needs more compulsive eaters who will get analysis and turn their excess energy into gifts of greatness. Ignorance is an evil we all have at sometime in our lives, but if we are open-minded and willing to change, we will progress and can do dynamic things. We try to escape by eating food but we don't solve anything. We are sick and need help. Why not try to rid ourselves of neurotic traits, but don't forget to give ourselves credit for our mature ones?

Most overeaters hate themselves. Even if they live alone and have no one to criticize them, they still hate themselves. Our relatives and outsiders criticize us, but we are our own worst enemy and judge. We find it difficult to discipline ourselves or find pleasure in anything but eating. We cannot concentrate for long on any one constructive job. We are all mixed up. We seem unable to change, but change can come. Self-pity will no longer be our cry. We can learn to fight it and laugh at our mistakes and change them. Helping someone less fortunate is always a good way to overcome self-pity. To point out our good traits and give ourselves credit is another way. Being humble enough to go and ask for help from various sources is another.

An overeater is behaving like a baby. He puts things in his mouth when he shouldn't. Even a baby can wait four hours between bottles so we should be able to wait four hours between each meal if we eat the right foods that will sustain us.

We also exaggerate things far out of proportion. We notice our reactions and then feel guilty. We compare ourselves too much with others. We must learn to let our emotions loose, talk about them and get them out so we won't have to "go eat about them." Too much of anything no matter how much we enjoy it is no good. We need variety to keep our perspective.

Most of us overeaters are not completely honest with ourselves. We sometimes diet and keep a faithful chart of foods to show our doctor or others. We forget to write down the tastes and snacks which could easily contain as many calories as another meal. No wonder we don't lose weight. Some of us eat without thinking. And sometimes we are so mixed up emotionally we don't know what we really ate.

Sometimes we hate ourselves so much we really don't want to have success. We don't feel we are worthy of success and happiness. That is why we must get control of our thinking and love ourselves before we can stay on a proper eating plan for any lasting length of time.

When we are ready to become honest with our neurosis, then we must be willing to take the next step and stop blaming other things and other people for our troubles. We can begin to become effective and efficient on some important endeavor. Nature itself wants us to be healthy and sound so we have everything good going for us. The way we look upon life sets the pattern for our actions.

We can stop hating and blaming ourselves. When we were born we did not have a choice of our environment. These things were there and we reacted to them as we grew. As children we could not pick the parents we needed for our fulfillment, but as adults we can overcome some of the neurotic tendencies handed down to us. Going to school and having new experiences with teachers and fellow students can have a big effect on our emotional lives.

All of us have guilt feelings at times. After guilt, we feel ashamed of ourselves and then feel inferior. Some of us feel so strongly about these normal feelings we overeat, since we don't know how to handle them. It is an escape from facing ourselves.

We have thin skin; we are easily hurt. That is why we never get the success we deserve. We must learn to fight back at life's obstacles in a way that will help us. We try to be like others but find it difficult. All of these feelings started with guilt. If we weren't feeling guilty we wouldn't blame ourselves for our failures. We are the victims of repression and past experiences.

The lies we were told about sex, religion, and other subjects helped make us the neurotic that we are today. Some of us overeaters have to give up all the old ideas about God, the Church, and religion. We have to get our own new beliefs in these things, so we can accept and use them as tools in our lives for future happiness. Things our parents told us or failed to tell us about sex also came to be a vital part of our frustrations. We must read all we can and discuss with others openly this subject in order to get out all our inhibition about sex. Sex, death, and religion are the least talked about subjects, and they are three very important subjects we cannot avoid forever.

Inferiority sometimes shows itself in persons who outwardly act superior. This is our cover-up, what we want to keep hidden. Many beautiful women act superior when they really feel inferior. They want to be liked for themselves, not for their bodies. Most people of this type feel guilty about not coming up to standards set by themselves or others. We should be happy that we are neurotic because if channeled correctly, we can overcome these feelings by accomplishing goals we never dreamed we could achieve. We can at least let go of the past and shine out with the true personality we really should have.

Most of us feel we deserve better than we get so we have a repressed superiority. Until we get the courage to know and be our true selves, we will remain unhappy. As a child we did not react like our playmates. We may have been bashful or "stand-offish." We got our feelings hurt easily and cried often. We craved love but rarely felt loved. We ran away from trouble instead of fighting to overcome it. Our social life was very unsuccessful. We tried to do things others did not do so we could feel proud of ourselves. We let others run over us instead of sticking up for our rights. We avoided parties and other places where we had to be with people. Today we are following the same patterns, but we no longer have to. We are not the child of the past — unless we still want to be. We can reach out and enjoy the glorious experiences of living as others do. We have the capacity for success far beyond our dreams. Our happiness can come and be truly effective if we only reach out to grab life's opportunities.

When we realize our worthiness and talents, then we can have the courage to share ourselves with the world. What others have done, we can do also. We have a lot of hidden power in us, a strong force that can react to life and people in a very successful way. This can be a blessing in disguise. Self-pity can go out the window and we can make our hidden talents work for us. The fear of not being accepted or approved has stopped us from going ahead on some of life's worthwhile challenges. We can get the courage to change.

If we felt unwanted as children, or were denied affection, or teased or were poor students, we tend to carry these feelings of inferiority into our adult lives. We are still being influenced by guilt feelings of childhood over which we had no control. Now that we realize this, we can stop punishing ourselves and grow to be the creative people we want to be. *Our eating problems can diminish.*

We can stop sacrificing the valuable hours we have to live, and depriving ourselves of happiness that we really deserve. We can recognize the superior qualities in ourselves and channel them into satisfying lives. When we recognize that we are very worthy human beings, our self-consciousness will go away.

When we repeat our mistakes continually, nature is telling us to do something. We don't mean to make mistakes, even when they repeat themselves. This is the subconscious mind calling for a change. We must heed it if we want to get well and accept ourselves as worthy human beings.

When we dislike someone it is usually because we are jealous, or see our own faults in that person. Sometimes another person reminds us of someone we disliked as a child. It is by our mistakes that we reveal ourselves. These are the hints that challenge us to change.

A compulsion to overeat is really an obsession to change our lives, but we are fighting the progress. If we fight our need to improve, we overeat. If we dwell on any one subject which we feel is not wholesome, we might turn to food. Sometimes we overeat so much we feel unworthy of mingling with others or being accepted anywhere. The only solution is to dig out our compulsions and obsessions; discuss them with ourselves, with God and with another person, to discover the exact nature of our trouble. Just the act of going this far sometimes erases many guilt feelings. Often these are the roots of our whole trouble.

Since compulsions stem from our own thoughts and actions, we have the power to get rid of them. Each time we give in to them, the habit becomes harder to get rid of.

If we become tired easily, it is usually because we have eaten too many refined carbohydrates and not enough protein, or it is because we can't face our lives as they are and want to escape by being inactive.

When we get rid of our neurotic tendencies, we can rid ourselves of fatigue and have a new zest for living.

Most of us eat more than necessary to maintain a healthy body and provide the energy we need. We can diet and lose weight, but unless our conflicts are brought out into the open, we are likely to have other physical symptoms appear such as headaches, skin rashes, colds, backaches, and many others. Pills might relieve them temporarily but they are not a cure. We must be willing to face reality and cope with it. "Action" is the magic word.

Sometimes a thorough analysis is not necessary. Some people get relief by counseling with a minister, doctor or friend who can be trusted. Someone who will not condemn or judge the neurotic is a must.

Our compulsive eating problems come from past or present temperaments, habits, environments, training or personality. We did not choose any of these knowingly so we can stop blaming ourselves right now. Handicaps for various physical reasons such as weak eyes, crippled limbs, deafness, inability to speak, and other things can tend to produce a compulsive overeater.

People can change and can be helped but they must believe it! Tolerance and understanding besides forgiveness of ourselves, are all necessary steps for recovery. We can now change our present lives and go ahead with a positive control over our own future.

We must be sure we are ready for success. Sometimes unexpected achievement can make us so emotional we don't believe it or cannot accept it. We usually expect defeat and failure because it was a habit of our past. We can think and practice thoughts of success in order to obtain and keep success. We all need an outlet or hobby besides our daily routine of life. Sometimes these various interests can even become financially profitable later in our lives, giving us less need to overeat.

As I write this book, I think of a hobby I had many years ago. It was cake decorating. I started out small, but after demonstrating my hobby at a Church Mother's Club hobby show, I was told by many people that I was good enough to be a professional. I went down to a local bakery the following day. I got a job starting with pay of $1.00 an hour. Within three years, I was receiving $2.50 an hour. After working in a bakery part time, I built up my own business and decorated lots of sheet cakes and wedding cakes in my own home. I felt a little guilty about making cakes because I preached "sweets and starches are harmful," to even the normal eater. When I began writing this book, I was thinking about giving up this original hobby. But just at that time I read another book which said one should never give up a satisfying talent. I get a sense of importance and esteem from decorating cakes beautifully. Also, it gives our family extra money for luxuries. I will probably keep on decorating cakes. But I have had to fight the compulsion to eat some custard or lemon filling or taste the icing. I've even been tempted to give up the business so I wouldn't binge. But I later realized the craving for sweets was not my problem, but the tensions and pressures of life as a whole. Now, after group therapy and learning to understand myself, I can decorate cakes, make all kinds of pastries for my family and not feel a desire to eat any of them. It was all a matter of changing my attitude about food and its importance in my life.

I also found another talent. I can write this book to help other people. I can now see where I made many of my mistakes in life and can get a more sensible view instead of being so emotional about everything. I have resolved to think differently. Each time I fight to improve myself, I feel like a worthy person. If I do not fight but run away from life's battles, I'll never be able to control my future.

We must constantly be prepared to guard against rejection, hurt, shock, or unpleasant experiences. We must have a Higher Power ready to help meet our needs. We must remember that all neurotic traits can be cured. Nothing is too big for us to change or improve. We must not try to run away from ourselves by turning to food and overeating. This produces no permanent cure; not even a temporary one. It makes things worse — not better. Remember one bite of some wrong food can set us off on a "binge." We can rid ourselves of emotional immaturity by controlling our eating. Once we do this, we will be more free, and surprisingly happy.

Resistance to therapy is the biggest drawback for neurotics. We must be sure we want to get rid of our childish ways and handicap symptoms. We must handle this resistance with determination and patience. It took us a long time to get this way and we can't expect to change overnight. Some other areas, besides the mind, that should be treated for neurotics are: blood pressure, vitamin deficiency, diet in general, lack of exercise, social contacts, free-time outlets, sex life, and spiritual life.

When we are generally miserable, we need the best therapy and should start searching by joining therapy groups, reading books, and counseling, to achieve a new perspective. We must get down to business and do something! We must love ourselves properly—no one else will. We have the right to be a person. We need to be open to new thoughts on how to develop our potential personality.

Writing a list of things we want to change or need to change in our lives is a good start toward our recovery. A solution always can be found if we keep looking for it. We tend to excuse ourselves for physical handicaps more than emotional ones, but they really fall in the same category.

Resistance to change is the biggest drawback. We should attempt to bring our weak abilities up to the level of our strong ones. Every weakness in our lives can become a challenge to do better. Being ashamed or afraid of a handicap or neurosis is childish. We are not at fault and should have no guilt feelings about them. They are only cries for help which we can meet by giving ourselves a chance to grow and mature like others. We can make ourselves as happy as we want to be. Once we pay attention to our neurotic needs, we are given a chance to effectively get busy and change them. Everything is in our favor for emotional security. We can learn to look back and laugh at our old pitiful self. What fools we were! We could have had serenity years ago—if only we had known!

DOCTORS CANNOT HELP SOME OVEREATERS

Doctors may help some overeaters stay on a diet for a period of time, but some patients have such an obsession for food that they will not, or cannot stay on a diet, for any lasting length of time. Because of emotional problems, they sooner or later indulge in compulsive eating or "binges."

I have a deep concern for overweight people who are compulsive overeaters. I am not a professional weight advisor, but I have had over 6 years study and experience working with these unhappy people. I understand and help them to a happier life, because I have arrested the "disease" of compulsive overeating myself.

If doctors could take time, or have their nurses phone diet patients between appointments to find out if they are doing O.K., perhaps the overeater would not resent so much the great amount of money they have to pay out in order to lose weight. They would feel the doctor's personal concern for their welfare. Doctors can help patients' progress, by being personally interested in the results. Many overweight people are resentful about life in general and are negative about being unable to lose weight.

Doctors who have a deep concern for the patients' welfare could tell them to get more sleep, more exercise, take supplementary vitamins, and to read something of a positive nature, so that the patient feels the doctor's special interest. They can also suggest that overweight patients should get some counseling for their emotional needs from ministers, psychiatrists or therapy groups.

Doctors sometimes do not realize that the compulsion to eat bread is the biggest reason some people gain weight. When the patients who are compulsive eaters are allowed 1 slice of bread a day, it is a constant battle for them to control their desire for more. At times they will go ahead and eat two or more pieces hoping that they won't gain weight. The doctor cannot understand why no weight is lost, and becomes disappointed with the lack of progress. A doctor who criticises a fat patient in any way does him only harm, thinking it will shock him into dieting. Resentments for the criticism only makes the miserable fat person go home and eat more.

Doctors should stop treating the symptom (fat) and get to the cause (anxiety).

I have had two diabetic patients in my groups who were so compulsive on eating bread, that they would rather keep their illness and fat than give up their bread. Others had illnesses such as high blood pressure, and they could not give up bread, which is a form of security to them. They keep damaging their health even though they realize it means an earlier death. Doctor's diets are for the purpose of helping people, but they do absolutely no good unless the patient is willing to follow them.

Here are just a few amounts of fattening foods admittedly consumed by former members of my clubs, which will give doctors the idea of how compulsive some people are. They could eat a whole bag of cookies, a whole loaf of French or raisin bread, half a dozen pastries, three or four servings of hot or cold cereal, five or six candy bars, a half gallon of ice cream, a whole recipe of pudding, a whole pie, half a cake, a box of crackers, a bag of potato chips, a bag of pretzels, and many large amounts of other refined carbohydrates. These amounts were consumed in one day according to the compulsion of the overeater at that time. Other obese people don't "binge", they just eat one meal a day — ALL DAY LONG!

Note that none of these foods are healthful ones. None are vegetables, proteins, or fruits. All are high in refined carbohydrates. That is the reason I recommend that the compulsive eater give them up entirely until he reaches his goal. Then, and only then, can he attempt to eat like a normal person. This suggests the value of group therapy or weight clubs.

Here are a few healthful foods that compulsive eaters can binge on when they are trying to lose weight; eggs, cheese, meat, carrots, celery, and fruits. The need for overeating any kind of food proves that the compulsive eaters will remain overweight unless they get their emotions under control and change their way of life. Then they will not have to "eat about anything."

In my experience working with compulsive overeaters, most club members who have lasting success are the ones who completely gave up all man-made sweets and starches, which were usually their "binge" foods. Some of these ladies have changed their dress size from size 20 or more to a size 10 or less in a year's time. Their skin at first becomes wrinkled, but after a reasonable period of high protein diet, it tightens up. A few rare members of weight clubs have been able to eat ½ cup portions of everything the family ate and lose weight, but they usually had a vital spiritual life to keep them serene. For some this is satisfying, but I believe for health reasons our bodies need more than one half cup of protein and other good foods at each meal. The overeater has become used to the feeling of being full, so he needs bulk foods such as lettuce, celery, etc., to fill him up. Extra vegetables help for better health because they contain many essential vitamins.

If a doctor is a practicing Christian, he can do wonders by praying for and with his fellow Christian fat patients. Faith in God and doctors are essential to the compulsive person's complete recovery. It can lift their morale and make them feel they are important individuals. Thousands of dollars are spent yearly by fat people on regular doctors and weight doctors, hoping they can lose weight. These individuals don't realize that they have the power, if they would only receive the therapy of understanding themselves. Then they could change their negative eating habits into a more positive outlet. The future can be one of lasting joy and fulfillment.

GROUP THERAPY HELPS COMPULSIVE EATERS

In group therapy the overeater can begin to understand the reasons for his obsession to overeat. He can become the person he would like to be. He will be able to first accept himself as he is; and get the courage to change in many constructive ways. Most overweight people have a poor image of themselves and even when they desperately think they want to lose weight, they cannot picture themselves thin. Self-improvement and therapy type groups can be some of the biggest assets in an overeater's life. Others share their hopes and strengths so they can also change negative overeating to positive actions. Sharing gives them a strong incentive to lose weight. Competition and good examples in the group help those who still suffer. Friends are made, and the overeater gets away from self-pity, depression or other frustrations which make him turn to food for comfort.

Therapy meetings once a week are an overeater's insurance in abstaining from old habits. Members share their self-discipline ideas with each other. Phone calls or letters are very helpful. Members feel important in their own right. Members volunteer to share their successes and failures in dealing with their difficulties. Inhibitions go and members let the group know just how they really feel about life. Each person is accepted and loved as he is. They give encouragement to each other.

"For the moment all discipline seems painful rather than pleasant; later it yields the peaceful fruit of righteousness by those who have been trained by it." Hebrews 12:11.

This Bible verse is very fitting to be read at therapy group meetings. In groups for Self-improvement, there is nothing more important than learning self-discipline.

We have to correct our past mistakes because when we did wrong, we didn't like ourselves, we felt guilty. We can get rid of this guilt only by discipline or change. We can do this by sharing with others in the group and by praying to God, asking for His help.

Secondly, we must accept discipline willingly. If we don't, we will continue our feeling of self-pity, disappointment, and failure when we don't lose weight. If we neglect self-discipline, we sin against ourselves. Suffering can become a form of discipline when we accept it and learn from it. There are many times when we have overeaten and even said aloud, "Oh God! Why did I do that? What are you trying to tell me? Help me not to make the same mistakes!"

Thirdly, there is discipline in training. We must train ourselves to give up fattening foods, over-sleep, laziness, and other comforts of a harmful nature in order to get the slim, healthful body we desire. We must discipline ourselves by exercising to tighten flabby skin and muscles. We must have a daily reading of self-improvement books and literature. We must choose these disciplines, because without them we cannot reach our desired goals.

All three of these disciplines are necessary for the Christian's progress. When we correct our faults we can thank God that we have not destroyed ourselves completely. When frustrations do come into our lives, we can learn from them that God's grace is sufficient to overcome them. We know that when we are searching for release and knowledge, we can be fulfilled.

All kinds of self-improvement can come to us through a good therapy group. The only way to mature physically, mentally and spiritually is with discipline.

1. Regular and prompt attendance at meetings.
2. Daily spiritual study and prayer.
3. Acceptance of some kind of responsibility in the group.
4. Sharing personal experiences which will help others.

It is much easier to keep a disciplined private life if one knows others in the group are doing the same. This lends support to the group for continuance and success. We must not "let the group down" by lack of self-discipline in any way, especially by eating. Gaining weight is a sin in a self-improvement club. But sins can be forgiven if the forfeit is paid and weight gain is lost.

If we want to achieve goals of any kind, we must do so by giving up certain habits which are undesirable. We can then go forward toward our goal.

Belonging to a group gives a person a sense of wholeness. We are trying to satisfy our needs by joining a group. We desire to belong to something which is deeply helpful to us. Some kind of group in which we can be a vital part to satisfy our lack of maturity, is needed. The quality of the group is more essential than the size. A group is most effective with eight to twelve members.

A group of a few people truly concerned about each others' needs can do a wonderful job of opening up new lives for all members. This can be done by participation in all the group's activities. Even the shy person can be drawn out and helped by others. He participates because he feels accepted and has a new meaning to his life. He begins to feel that life is meaningful, vital, and changing for the better.

Groups help us become objective about ourselves and able to honestly face areas in our lives which need changing. We need to come to see our real selves so the group can aid us by helping us practice self-acceptance and honesty. We begin to see that all members make mistakes and we too can keep trying to improve. First we must see our own mistakes and ask God to forgive them. After we know He does forgive us, we still must forgive ourselves. The group can help us by accepting us just as we are. Courage to change begins to be "catching" from the group. Because others are improving, we become able to improve also. It is the courage of the group as a whole that helps members to lose weight and keep it off.

We can give up all kinds of "goodies" when we know others are doing it. We dare to correct our bad eating habits because we know others in the group are supporting us. We get an inner motivation which can encourage us to continue on our road to success.

Prayer is vital in a group and in private. It can be a tremendous source for accomplishment. The sharing of insights and experiences, good or bad, can be very helpful to group participation. Self-centeredness becomes less and less for each member. In group fellowship each member finds courage to go towards his goals. We become objective about ourselves and aware of a need for deep spiritual growth. We become no longer satisfied with life as it is and look back and wonder at how our families and friends put up with us. God constantly confronts us with ways of facing our inner lives. The group is one way of facing our true selves.

"If we say that we have no sin, we deceive ourselves, and the truth is not in us. If we confess our sins, He is faithful and just to forgive us our sins and to cleanse us from all unrighteousness." (I John 1, V 8 & 9)

"Therefore confess your sins to one another, and pray for one another, that you may be healed." (James 5;16)

These Bible verses give us the idea that group therapy is beneficial. It is not enough to confess our sins to God but to another person or persons. To us modern people, this seems unnecessary, but if experienced it can do wonders. This kind of confession can be successful only in a close-knit fellowship where love is felt toward all members. To admit our faults humbles us, but it also strengthens us. We know no one is perfect, so it should be helpful to admit one's faults to others. If we find a group which can be honest among themselves, we will be more willing to be honest with ourselves in private and confess our own deep needs.

Some Christians really never feel forgiven even when they are told that God forgives them. That is because they can't forgive themselves. Here is where the group comes in. Groups of a loving quality accept and love us so we can learn to forgive and accept ourselves too. Freedom comes after we confess our shortcomings and feel accepted by love from others. When we share our problems we gain new strength and wisdom to go forward. We admit freely and openly that we are what we are and that we need help. We admit that we are compulsive overeaters and we need help from God and others.

Psychologists often relate our life's problems to the four evil influences of life — fear, hate, inferiority, and guilt. Guilt, which is abnormal, is an enemy. But the normal guilt we should have helps us to change for better personalities because it informs us of the need for a change. When we repress real guilt feelings, we can become emotionally disturbed. We feel guilty about overeating, but this is only the minor problem to greater guilts that we don't want to face. This must be repeated—OUR PROBLEMS OF OVEREATING ARE NOT OUR FAT OR OUR OBSESSION FOR FOOD. Our problems are deep within our unconscious mind and emotions. This is why therapy groups are so beneficial to help individuals face their real problems in life which can later help them to lose weight and keep it off.

Group confession is more beneficial to an individual than if he confesses to a single counselor. In a group, he feels love and acceptance from several but from a counselor he might feel judged or feel a lack of love. The professional counselor rarely admits his own shortcomings, consequently a client may feel unworthy and inferior. A group experience can bring a release from all our past repression and bring a new life of freedom, to become a real person.

"Above all hold unfailing your love for one another, since love covers up a multitude of sins." (Peter 4;8)

This Bible verse is meaningful because we all need love and approval from others. We constantly strive toward this aim. When others approve of us we become happy. We sometimes put on an act just so we will be accepted, but in a group for self-improvement we don't have to put on a mask. We can be our true selves and show exactly how we feel. Our fellow members look into our hearts, not at our fat bodies. Even when we show inner conflicts and doubt we are still accepted in the group and loved. The unlovely person needs love more than the lovely one. It is great to be a member of a fellowship where there are no barriers or pretensions; where one can open up freely and let out his real feelings and emotions.

This gives personal growth to all members. When some members find it impossible to share with the group, the other members find it difficult to help them. After he listens and realizes that he is not the only one with his type of problem he will open up in order to get help. It then becomes a wonderful experience to feel that he is still loved in spite of all his shortcomings; just because he is a person.

God's love can become more real through the love within a group. Members feel that if the group accepts them, then God must. God mediates His love through persons. Exceptional talents or virtues are not necessary for love and approval but sometimes in groups, members find new abilities they never dreamed of having. In order to accept others and God we must first accept ourselves.

We need the support of each member for our own success. We should not only ask others to pray for us, but we should pray for them during meetings and in private. In this way prayer becomes real and helpful. Spiritual power comes to us through others who share our faith. We need others and they need us. Strength and courage come to us from our fellow members. When temptation to eat comes, we can phone or talk to someone or ask them to pray for us. Spiritual support is a need of every man. Our progress depends on the support we get and give in the group. The fellowship of togetherness promotes healing in many areas of our lives. Sometimes in our families there are barriers which make it difficult to help each other, so we attend group meetings for our deep level needs. After we feel the group has helped us, our family barriers can vanish. We can give confidence to others after we gain it ourselves. Trust in a group is essential. Each of us desires trust so we can learn to trust others. It propels us to new heights and mature experiences.

Love and trust that are felt in a group are the main source of release and healing that takes place in the lives of members. There is no fear in love. Members no longer feel rejection, or disapproval. To trust and be trusted is essential for the overeater's happiness.

Fears of other members betraying confidences sometimes creeps into our minds, but if we realize that love can accept us, our fears of gossip soon vanish. Each person shares, and the group must be trusted. When we feel several people trusting in us, we gain new heights of power which continue as we search along the pathway to success. When the group expects us to be trustworthy, then we realize that God trusts us so love can flow through us.

If we have faith and love in a group, we can communicate our thoughts to others. We must "talk out" our fears, doubts, resentments and guilt feelings. The first step toward losing weight and keeping it off is to bring these things out into the open and talk about them. This may not be easy for some, but it becomes easier when others have shared. There are always compulsive talkers in every compulsive eating group. They can help others by relating their frustrations and talking them out. The group is a sounding board. Members sooner or later open the door to their inner selves and get a full release from what used to make them overeat. They find a new security which enables them to *get well.*

The person who does not share has a fear of rejection, but as time goes on he will change that fear to one of trust and acceptance. Those who feel compelled to talk too much will find security enough to listen to others, and those who remain silent will find freedom to express their thoughts and feelings openly. When they believe others will understand their true feelings, their fear of speaking will vanish. Courage to express ourselves in a group is essential to successful recovery. Both silent prayer and audible prayers are essential to Spiritual growth. Being able to talk about God or pray to God openly is one of the most wonderful experiences a person can have. We can become free to communicate with each other and God.

Concern for others is essential for our own growth. Being concerned about ourselves is useless unless we love others. It has a healing power far beyond any other kind of healing. Joy and fellowship in groups can lead the whole world to lasting peace.

THE ART OF UNDERSTANDING YOURSELF

This chapter is especially prepared by the author after reading the above named book three times. Mrs. Brians was so impressed with Dr. Cecil Osbornes' book, "The Art of Understanding Yourself", that she received permission from him to use the ideas from his book by adding her own thoughts as she went along. Dr. Osborne is pastor of the First Baptist Church, in Burlingame, California. He is also a counselor for many "mixed up" emotional people outside his church. He can be contacted through his church or through Yokefellows Inc., 209 Park Rd., Burlingame, Calif. 94010.

Tests for group therapy are available through Yokefellow by special request from leaders of weight clubs, or other organizations which are helping to improve members. Write and ask for information about kinds of tests and costs.

Also copies of the above book and many others like it are available to individuals or clubs through Yokefellows Inc. Write for book list.

If I want to stop being miserable, I must stop thinking about myself— what I like— what people ought to do—then I will be at peace and not be so wretched. I will forget about myself, what I want or what others should do. I will correct my faults and be happy—I can. No one really knows me—only myself. I have a need to share, but I also sometimes get release talking to myself and God.

Some of us are not sure God listens and that is why we do not pray. Believe He listens—pray—and He will listen and you will get help. The real need of most men is for someone to listen. God's love is mediated through persons.

Be honest with yourself and God. If you hate your life, tell God, He knows anyway. Admit you need help. Admit who you are angry with. Get it out and talk about it. Results are dependent on how deeply you are motivated to talk things out.

28

Sin is not just lies, theft, immorality, dishonesty, but sin is less than perfection. It is rejection of God—falling short of what we feel God wants us to be. It is important to have good motives. Sin is the clever rationalization by which we seek escape from facing ourselves.

Sometimes an outsider will make us feel more understood than our own families. One hour a week in church is not enough to provide us with answers to our deepest spiritual needs. We need to know God through other persons. God is interested in every concern and in every detail of our lives. He is interested in small things as well as big ones. All life is sacred.

If we eat right, exercise and have a daily devotional life we will come to accept and even like ourselves. We will be proud of our whole selves and feel at peace with the world. When things are going well, don't be an injustice collector. Don't prod or nag someone. You don't have to punish yourself or others. You don't have to get your feelings hurt. Remember you are a person. You don't have to try to think of ways to be rejected. You bring most of your suffering on yourself.

If we feel guilty, sometimes it is because of unattainable standards of conduct imposed upon us by others, or because we feel rejected or inadequate. Rejected people sometimes feel guilty, but they don't want to. Sometimes when we feel unloved we feel bad. We are worthy of love and we must make a valiant effort to become a mature adult and then we will not feel rejected or have self-pity.

Learn to pray and relate to God as a loving Heavenly Father; not as you remember your earthly father. That's where we get fouled up in our not believing in God, because we think of God as our earthly father and if our Dad did not love or show love, we cannot love God. We must change this feeling, because there are lots of men in the world who are capable of showing love. We must believe there is a God who loves us. There is no limit to spiritual growth. Miraculous things have taken place in people's lives because of faith in God.

No one makes a significant change in personality or life situations until he is motivated by some kind of pain. Suffering is a sign of the availability of energy to transform yourself. You have had more than your share of pain and now it is time to change your worldly self into a spiritual being. Suffering is nature's method of indicating a mistaken attitude or way of behavior and every moment of suffering is the opportunity for growth—so change—do something about your suffering! Learn to communicate with others and a Higher Power.

Learn to handle hostility, and problems will clear up. This is done through a mature form of prayer. Physical symptoms disappear.

Deal with the underlying cause and acknowledge hostility. As we relate to ourselves, in love and trust in God, our need for physical pain will vanish. Try to love people who have not liked you or who you don't like. Pray for them. Then you can accept and love them.

Don't cover up your feelings of inadequacy with a pretense of superiority which you do not really feel. You will not feel lonely after you break through the barrier of fear of rejection. When you reveal yourself, you will find yourself accepted and loved at a new level. It comes only by love—Love for God—Love for others. It takes away all loneliness.

As children, if we never got compliments or love in any way, and were told we were stupid and many other hurtful things—we grew up with problems. You must be willing to uncover some of your deeply buried emotions. Surrender all your hostility to God. God is within you and part of you. You will be more tolerant of others, and not try to make their turmoil yours. Hostility and fear and guilt can be replaced by love. Intense fear of our emotions prevents us from being able to give and receive love. We don't have to bury or hide emotions. Admit them, then you can change them. We can show fear. We must love ourselves before we can love others, so accept yourself first.

Many neurotic individuals prefer to endure the misery of their present situation than risk the uncertainty that would come with change. When we resist prayer and meditation, we are unconsciously afraid of what God is trying to reveal to us.

Try to lose the fear of being with people—surrender your martyr complex and you will reveal a remarkable sense of self-acceptance. The person who is not anchored in God can offer no resistance to the physical needs of the body. It is a sin to hurt our bodies in any way.

Believe this or not—Everyone is spending at least 50% of his psychic energy keeping repressed memories below the level of consciousness. We try to avoid anxiety—if this anxiety is energy, it can be made available for creative living. We can change our lives and destinies. Sometimes we avoid social events because they make us feel inferior and insecure.

It is safe to say that all anxiety-laden behavior stems not from a rationally thought out process—but from emotional factors, and that usually roots back to our childhood.

The reason we don't want to change our attitude is because we feel we might create a greater anxiety—we must understand our basic natures first, before we can willingly change our attitude or actions. Our problems of physical sickness are only the outer symptom of a very strong anxiety and need. When we feel threatened by some situation, we think we can endure the anxiety by getting sick, which only makes us worse off. Being bedridden or unhealthy seems to dull our senses and then we cannot cope with the situation. We have guilt and inferiority feelings. The only way we can get out of our sickness is to admit we are powerless and are ready to turn to God or a Higher Power as we understand Him. The admission of the fact we are powerless is absolutely essential. The most dangerous way to handle hostility is to repress it. We must first admit it, then release it to God in complete abandonment.

Many sick people think they want to get well, but their subconscious still wants to remain sick. Peace can come only when we surrender the emotions to God. Mixed emotions to get well or stay sick are ever present with us. This plays a large part in our human relations and has a lot to do with our physical well being or lack of it.

A person may say "I don't have any problems—I just have a headache or pain of some other kind," but it's probably because he can't pinpoint the real underlying problem. His anxiety sometimes comes because of his parents or environment, but we can look at the true nature of emotions. Aggression can express itself in two ways; it can be openly hostile and possibly destructive, or it can be creative, a drive to change circumstances which build and produce good things.

Many people suffering from strong anxiety would much prefer to have an illness, keep fat, or undergo treatment for health problems, than to face the fact that the problem is emotional or spiritual in origin. We can endure physical pain rather than choose emotional conflict. Man is body, mind, and spirit; what affects one, affects all. If we think about our physical body too much, we suffer. If we try to be overly spiritual, we become fanatics and get little real help, and if we study only the mind, that is not enough either. We need an equal balance of all three to make us "whole" persons.

Guilt, whether real or false, can be handled in only two ways; it must be forgiven or punished. If we cannot secure forgiveness, we must find a way to punish ourselves physically, mentally or circumstantially. But then, it is not God who is punishing, but the condemnatory self. We must achieve emotional and spiritual maturity. We can read good literature, communicate with others who will help us, change our attitude about ourselves, others, and God.

We can pray and turn to Him who made us, and admit we are emotionally "sick". Then, and only then can we ever expect to get completely "well" from our compulsive personalities. We must learn that it is good to like, and yes, to love ourselves properly. God wants us to love ourselves first, before we try to love others, because this is the only successful way to do it. How can we love others if we hate ourselves? You are a person, created by God, and you were given this life to live in abundance and happiness, so it is up to you to do your part to make this life the best one you can.

Just being aware of inner conflicts is not always sufficient; next we must accept the fact that we feel them, then we need to talk them out before taking action to change them.

We can be free of our alienation from people and our need for being sick, if we re-establish ourselves in a loving relationship with God and man. We can come to regard ourselves as forgiven and acceptable. We can learn to trust our emotions, our friends, and God. Anxiety is the absence of love. We can only be forgiven for emotion after we admit having it. We must confess to ourselves we have it—then to God. We know God forgives us, but we must also forgive ourselves. Avoiding a problem solves it only temporarily. Rationalizing is also an escape. Headaches and other physical symptoms such as stomach ache or pain is only an escape from our real problem.

The only creative solution is to seek out the answer by removing the anxiety. Time doesn't always diminish our feelings of guilt. Sometimes we think time will cure everything, but it doesn't. Sometimes there are not only guilty acts, thoughts, or attitudes, but the general feeling of "not measuring up". Anxiety can be creative if we let it be.

Visualization plays a vital part in effective prayer. If you want the will of God in your life, you can receive what you want if you visualize it. Expect to get it. You can be well if you picture yourself well. You can see your healthful self now as a happy person. We only have to reach for goals to achieve them. God is waiting for us to trust and believe Him. Then we can receive true success—blessing upon blessing—miracle upon miracle. We are not using God—but we must never want God's blessing without wanting Him. He wants our love and all these things shall be added to us as a matter of course. We must want God's will above our own. Not to want His will is to refuse to trust Him.

Part of the reluctance to want God's will is derived from fear that if we surrender to Him completely—we might have to give up some resentment or feeling or pleasure. Some of our difficulty springs from our stubborn egocentric way. We want our way and are afraid we will lose our freedom of choice or some of our individuality. It is basically losing our self-hood. Someone else would be running our lives, and we don't want that, even if that someone is God. To want God's full will is to rejoice and know that God is infinite love and wills the best for us, that we are willing to trust His way of running the universe; and that we want to experience the satisfaction of His Universal laws that operate on His behalf.

In prayer we receive what we want most earnestly. It may not be what we ask for, but it is what we want, for prayer is the soul's sincere desire, uttered or unexpressed. If what we ask for in prayer verbally conflicts the thing we want basically at the feeling level, we receive not what we ask for, but what we really want. If we ask to get well, but don't want to eat right, sleep enough, exercise, live right, we will not get well. Prayer is an effort to bring our stubborn, reluctant, egocentric wills into harmony with God's loving purpose. He wills best for us. When we can trust His wise and creative purposes for our lives, we will have then begun to pray effectively.

A person is not made up of acts, but of desires only. As is his desire, such is his resolve; as is his resolve such is the action he performs; what action he performs, that he procures for himself.

Failure to accept forgiveness and feel forgiven constitutes the greatest single problem for most people, though they may be partially or totally unaware of the basic difficulty. Few of us feel so fully cleansed and forgiven that we are able to forgive ourselves fully, and to forgive others. We all want and need love, and we must admit it. Then we can accept love. We feel guilt not only for what we have done, but often because of the shame over what has been done to us. We must acquire new spiritual resources with which to meet the issues of life. The accumulated stress of life, or some traumatic event, often triggers the old sense of self-rejection which is always present until we secure a sense of Divine forgiveness and are consequently able to forgive ourselves. It is the state of mind, the intent of the heart, which counts; not the words or the form in which the confession is framed. *"Therefore confess your sins to one another, pray for one another, that you may be healed."* True confession is painful. If it is not painful, it is not likely to be effective. *"He who does not love, does not know God—for God is Love."*

We cannot pray effectively unless we feel love, unconditional love, for everyone. Even our enemies. We are not condemned by our failures even if we fail over and over again; we must rise again and continue to follow the right life that we know is best for us. We are always accepted and forgiven. There is no limit to God's love and forgiveness. We are reluctant to confess to God because we are unable to believe deeply that God really forgives us instantly, without qualification. God is not like us—forgiving one or two failures or fifty. God is better—His love is infinite. If our concept of God is adequate, our prayer of confession will be adequate. Nothing we have done is so bad that He loves us less. Nothing good we have ever done is sufficient to cause Him to love us more. His love is a fixed and unchanging factor.

We must be honest with ourselves, so we can be then honest with God. If you feel hostility, tell Him so. Don't justify or rationalize it—just confess it. Confess the self-sufficiency which has caused you to depend upon yourself more than upon God. When you get beset with how you have been mistreated by others, the fault may be someone else's rather than your own, but REMEMBER—YOU ARE NOT RESPONSIBLE FOR WHAT PEOPLE DO TO YOU — BUT YOU ARE RESPONSIBLE FOR THE WAY YOU REACT TO THEM.

In confession, it is worse than a waste of time to recount the sins or failures of others. We cannot solve our problems by confessing the defects of others. Even if the other person is 90% wrong, our business is to examine our own guilt in the matter and confess it. There is no reason to condemn; only find the source of the problem. There is no more virtue in condemning oneself than in condemning others. If I do not forgive myself, it is because I refuse to accept His cleansing forgiveness. Do we have too much pride to accept Divine forgiveness?

Because our childhood feelings are still alive in us we tend to project onto God the feelings we had toward our parents. We may wonder if God is any more forgiving than they were. God is more ready to forgive than we are to receive forgiveness, and that the greater our sin the quicker He is to forgive us. When we react in hostility to what someone did or said, it is a threat to our security. Hostility usually stems from fear of being dominated, fear of being wrong, fear of something else, or fear of just ourselves. We must face this in all our relationships.

Sin is essentially a wrong against the self or another human being. It is not against God, but ourselves. The proper reaction to awareness of guilt is not self-hate but an active stimulation to do better. Self-hate itself is a great wrong. To hate ourselves is to despise one whom God loves; it is as much a sin as hating another person. Daily relationship with God in prayer and reading gives us the calm to deal with others in loving patience. God is against whatever is destructive for us so when we make a decision, ask this, "Is it constructive?"

Our guilt must be fully forgiven or we will find ways to punish ourselves. If our concept of God's forgiveness and love is adequate, we can accept his pardon and forgive ourselves. We cannot be forgiven by God unless we are willing to forgive others. We must be willing to pray for our enemies or those who hurt us, no matter what they have done. Our capacity to recive His love hinges upon our being willing to love. We are entitled to love ourselves properly. We are entitled to a healthy body, so we must keep striving for true success and keep it. The self is judging us constantly — we don't have to wait for the day of judgment. If our hearts do not condemn us we have confidence before God. Lying to ourselves or denying our true feelings or refusing to face up to our real selves is dishonesty. We are not fully sound and out of danger until we no longer are afraid of letting anyone know the truth about us.

Every maladjusted person is a person who has not made himself known to another human being, and in consequence does not know himself. When the problem of inner conflict has been resolved, the pain of guilt should cease. To be whole is to be open with God, through confession. We must release the pain of guilt to Him and accept His Divine forgiveness.

Stop punishing yourself by being sick. You don't have to be sick. Do everything you know is best to get yourself well. Change your eating habits, your living habits, your negative thinking and you will get well. Make yourself as attractive as you can. Smile, even if it hurts. Act in an acceptable manner and soon you'll feel well. Bring your disordered life under the control of the living Spirit in you. Deal with all matters of guilt to get a sense of forgiveness. All criticism is destructive whether expressed or only felt. We may label it constructive criticism, but the victim hears it as judgment. We can only change ourselves, and when we change, others tend to change in reaction to us.

God's love is extended unconditionally to all who receive it. God does not condemn us even when we fail. He accepts us even though we do not feel acceptable to ourselves. God's love and forgiveness are unchanging factors. Our "goodness" or "badness" do not affect these Divine laws in the slightest. God is not waiting to extend forgiveness and love until we repent; it is rather that we are incapable of accepting the grace He eternally extends until we repent. Love is the key—not advice. People only want and need guidance. Straighten your own life out first, before attempting to help others. Sharing with others gives us a sense of understanding and acceptance, we can begin to accept the forgiveness of God which has been available all along. Our capacity to deceive ourselves is enormous. Re-examine your motives for your feelings or actions which make you sick. False guilt stems from rejection in childhood—feeling unloved, unwanted and worthless. It registers on the mind as guilt. High goals set by other people for us register as guilt. Throw away standards others set for you and make your own. You are adult. Blame is unnecessary toward no one—even yourself. It is circumstances alone that cause things to happen. Offer your new true self to God.

Just because women are more emotional than men does not mean that they are less stable emotionally. Men and women are wired differently, emotionally and intellectually. Women unconsciously tend to preach and prod to discover strength in men and if possible to conquer them. A woman seeks control of the male by direct or indirect means, but the feminine part of her nature feels defeated and frustrated when she achieves the goal. She married him because of gentleness but now despises this very quality. Do you want victory—insist on being defeated or desire the last word? Men and women approach problems in an entirely different way, and it is no wonder that they find discussion either unfruitful or impossible. Man's interests are more general than specific.

Neurotic tendency in women will decrease when they have the desire to love their children more and not because they are forced to. Children would then not be something that interferes with more interesting things. Woman's security is wrapped up in her personality. Women frustrate men by being or appearing to be dominant. Dominance is the inner urge to control people or circumstances and aggression is the inner urge to change them. Men get frustrated from women being too emotional. Don't keep expecting perfection in your husband. He isn't perfect. Are any of us?

You don't have to keep proving yourself if you don't want to. You've won the battle of success. You've got your answers for getting well, so use them and be healthy. Stop fighting success. You deserve it. The more self-acceptance you get the less you need to dominate others or to get their approval. 80% of all our actions and decisions are motivated by unconscious inner needs. Most of our decisions are the result of totally unconscious drives.

Whatever you feel yourself to be at the center of your emotional nature, that is what you really are, and your actions will be in harmony with your self-concept. If you tell yourself repeatedly that you can get well, you will. It is as simple as that. We can change, but if you tell yourself that you can do nothing to get well, then stay sick and be miserable. It's up to you. You can change. We have an inner Divine capacity which enables us to be more than we are. We must not fear all deep feelings, and not fear God — don't bury it — bring it out. You can be a different person in mind and body and spirit. You can discover the highest potential, and act differently. There are untapped resources in all of us. We can love more, be more, achieve more, acquire more, and have more inner strength. Be willing to have His best for us. We can be vastly more than we are. We can have a new self image and act in harmony with that new concept. As our fear of rejection lessens, our own capacity for self-acceptance improves and we are on our way.

Act the way you want to feel and soon you'll feel that way. Be genuinely interested in people and in anything that matters to them.

MINISTER-COUNSELOR HELPS START SELF-IMPROVEMENT CLUB

After four years of being a member of Food-Alcoholics Anonymous, I decided that I wanted to go into deeper therapy in order to get rid of my compulsive eating and many other defects of my character.

In F.A. I was able to maintain a weight loss of 20 pounds, but with great difficulty, because I "fought" their spiritual program for recovery from compulsive overeating. I had not given up an occasional "binge" at times of stress or when I could not handle a situation or accept life as it was handed down to me.

I knew a minister who was also a marriage counselor — and I persuaded him to help me get a therapy group started. We set up weekly meetings in which we had twelve members. He talked about many problms of life including compulsive eating. The thing I liked about my friend Marvin was that he admitted his own shortcomings to the group. This alone gave us confidence to tell him our faults and enabled us to share our frustrations. He even admitted that he too was a compulsive overeater. At that time he looked about twenty or more pounds overweight.

Marvin told us a typical story of a compulsive overeater. One day he went into a big department store to pay something on his account, and as he entered he saw a necktie in the window that he liked. He asked a clerk to show it to him at closer range. The clerk was reluctant to take the necktie out of the window, and Marvin became provoked. He felt that since he was doing regular business with this store, he deserved the service of seeing any merchandise that he was interested in purchasing. The clerk became so uncooperative that Marvin went home angry. On the way home he bought a quart of chocolate milk and drank the whole thing because he had become so angry at the clerk.

We compulsive overeaters are the only ones who can understand a story like that. No normal eater gives in to his frustrations by eating extra food. I also liked Marvin because he had a deep faith in God, but did not kid himself into saying that he didn't have many frustrations in his ministry or private life. He had a tragedy in his younger years, and this helped him to have more empathy for others with problems. After a number of meetings with Marvin, he was transferred to another city, so I asked him to help me set up a format for the Self-Improvement Club which has been helping many for the last two years. We set up a 12 step recovery program based on the alcoholic people at these meetings. We changed the program enough to be suitable for the compulsive overeaters' needs. I became the leader and have led continuing groups. I learned from these therapy type meetings that many people have adult problems which stem from their childhood. As I read many helpful books and worked with others in my club, I realized that help can come from sharing experiences. The club began to purchase many recommended books which were loaned to members.

Marvin spent about one year in the other city church and then he received a call to be a counselor for alcoholics in a large city. He is now working with an Alcoholic Rehabilitation Center including about 80 members. He works mainly with groups but also with individual cases. As his clients come into his office for counseling, many do not know that he is also a minister. Many alcoholics feel they have been hurt by the church, and some have resentments toward religion, so Marvin does not "preach" to them. He talks to them at "gut" level. He is the most wonderful preacher I have ever heard because he is a real person and in his sermons is not afraid to tell the world just how he feels and believes.

Not long ago Marvin filled in at our church for a few weeks while we were waiting for a new minister to come. I took notes on his sermons. Here are a few thoughts on one about "The Hills" which I will share;

"To get through the day is a serious business and we need all the help we can get. If the *outlook* is bad, try the *uplook*. Here is how to get through the day: First, turn your attention to the high places (such as the hills) where you have been. Look for hope and renewal in the hills. Search for the good, retreat, and plan ahead. Love is the law of life and the law of life is sacrifice. We get a new strength from the hills which is not in the valley. We look up to them. The hills restore our sense of meaning in life. What is our life worth? What is our worth? We belittle ourselves and others too much. We must lift up our eyes to persons who can help us. Think of someone who has enriched our lives — some meaning — new strength — knowing the capacity for love. To understand all is to forgive all. We quickly condemn others but we need to love. Life is going up to the hills, but then we go down, but we don't have to stay there. We keep getting exposed to knowledge. We sometimes come to hate people who make us think, but if we keep the relationship long enough we will change our feelings about that person. We find strength from people we hate and they can help lift us up. We need to read good books. We need to hit the "bottom" to be able to climb to the top. We can get faith in ourselves when doubt seems to take over. We can share our smallness with a great or high person in our life and become tall ourselves. Being able to accept the "crumminess" in ourselves is the first step to greatness. We must accept the worst in others before we can accept ourselves. We must seek and find a mountain-top person for ourselves so that person can help us develop worthiness in ourselves. We need to know a dependable, authentic person. We must look to life and find our purpose in it. Love is the ultimate in life. Even when we hate, we want to be loved. That is what life is "all about!" Our lives will *never* run on an even plane. We'll have our ups and we'll have our downs. We fight this fact but we know it is true. The psychotic says two and two are five. The neurotic says two and two are four, but he can't stand it and makes life difficult for himself. The "isness" of life we cannot change. We are living what we experience and we had better accept it. We can create it, but we still have our ups and downs. We measure life by ups and downs.

Look at the average person as a whole. He has periods of success and failure — nothing goes right *all* the time. He has the capacity for love and hate, and he can accept the unlovely in others."

* * *

The most wonderful thing I learned about Marvin was, that after he had been working with the alcoholics a few months, he had lost all his excess weight and looked ten years younger. He finally had found a meaningful life work for himself. He was so busy helping others who needed him that he did not have time or take time to overeat. All of us have a purpose in this world. Some of us find it late in life. Some never seem to find it, and others are still searching. Life is a great experience and it is up to each one of us to decide what we are going to do about it, with it and in it.

HELPFUL MIXED IDEAS
FOR MIXED-UP COMPULSIVE EATERS

Good humor is not a trait of character. It is an art which requires practice.

Any good advice is trouble unless I believe and feel it will help me.

Overeating is a sign of insecurity and immaturity. I shall try to become more mature and secure by avoiding compulsive eating.

No one but myself knows what I ought to do; so I will do it.

We suffer because we feel inadequate. When you are in a state of confusion — get away from where you are — but don't take your troubles with you.

Most troubles after we are adults do not reside in life, but in us. We have no choice but to give vigorous attention to the correction of them.

If you don't agree with this book's way of living at least it's loused up your eating.

If you don't get better you get bitter.

This is easily done when you're having fun. Smile.

I must make up my mind to eat for health reasons more than taste.

Hunger pangs never get better, but they never get worse. Enjoy them because they are a sign of losing weight.

40

Depend on your Higher Power more than your scales.

Keep relaxed and you won't get so hungry.

I must give more love to others daily.

A diet is what you keep putting off while you keep putting on.

Obstacles are those terrifying things we see when we take our eyes off our goals.

It is better to feel empty and hungry than to feel bloated; too full, in pain, and too full of hate for yourself.

The alcoholic will give up all liquids that make him drunk — so I can give up all foods that make me fat.

Before eating something fattening ask yourself — "Is this food worth gaining weight for?"

Water is not fattening — it is temporary weight only.

Doing without breakfast can result in low-blood sugar level and you might crave more for lunch. At least have an egg for breakfast.

I will try to be honest with myself in my eating — because if I don't I hurt only myself.

When we judge others and play God — we act like the Devil.

If you don't take time to use the good odors such as perfume, deodorants, etc., at least keep the bad ones away by baths, brushing teeth, etc.

I must become what I need to be, as radiantly as possible.

Do I have self-pity often? How do I overcome this?

Why do we hate to pray and ask a Higher Power to help us? Because we are proud and want to do it ourselves or because we don't feel worthy of God's love?

I admit my will power is low and I am powerless over food and my life has become unmanageable.

Reading books of a helpful nature in many areas will help me to be a better person.

If you call someone before you take that first bite they might help you, but if you go ahead and eat you are headed for trouble.

Remember the time to call another compulsive eater is when you feel strong so you can help others.

Another time to call is when you feel weak; and need help yourself.

If you don't class yourself as a compulsive eater — you can judge for yourself — Surround yourself with your favorite sweets and starches and try some controlled eating. Try to take one serving and stop. This will be your answer as to how you control your eating or how compulsive you are.

The book can challenge me to change and improve myself in lots of ways besides weight loss.

This book can help me to feel accepted as I am with all my faults as well as my assets.

I will try to have more fun and stop taking life so seriously.

Yesterday is gone and I can live this day only — free from the past.

No one but me can make me stop overeating. I am the one who puts food in my mouth. No one ever forces me to overeat.

There is no shame in admitting I have an eating problem and I'm glad I can do something about it.

I will push my panic button and not let myself gain more than a few pounds before losing them again. This way I will be in control most of the time and can live with myself.

Phone calls have sustained many a faltering overeater on the verge of returning to unhappy eating habits.

We need a high enema to get rid of:
1. Secret revenge motives
2. Unnecessary duty patterns
3. Old despair attitudes
4. Unjustified guilt feelings
5. Unnecessary habits of worry

Do I really have a desire to stop eating compulsively?

Do I realize this is the only road to successful weight loss for any lasting length of time?

Instead of fleeing from my troubles in food, I must have patience to bear these burdens, thanking God that they are not worse. I will think of the discipline and good I can do to change them.

Those who seek a divorce are not at fault, nor can we ever hold them responsible until they know how to select a mate intelligently. Divorce comes only as a saturation point. They shouldn't be condemned but forgiven.

The result of your weight loss is rapid or slow according to the depth and thoroughness of your physical intent. You are required to work for the removal of fat with all your strength and soul.

Go back to what reason you overate — fight it and get rid of it.

Inside every fat girl there is a slim girl crying to get out. So let's help her escape!

Love is not anyone's possession. It comes into him or goes out of him, quickening him or leaving him much in the way life is received or disappears.

Nothing takes the place of confidence. Get some in yourself.

Do I eat to escape worries or troubles?

What can I do instead of eating?

Do I still eat when I'm not hungry?

Do I call someone instead of eating between meals?

Do I think about food too much?

I will try to eat slower and enjoy my food more.

I will try to be open-minded to everyone's ideas about losing weight.

I will catch my negative thoughts and try to change them to positive actions.

"Weighing in" weekly is a form of a Higher Power — it gives me a feeling of importance and knowing that I can be honest with myself.

I must be fearless and thorough from the very start or the result will become nothing.

I will remember this obsession is baffling and powerful and I need help.

I must discover the laws, the principles and the actions to take which will remove my difficulties. Then I will have no reason to overeat.

I must stop feeling guilty of the things I'm not, and do to the best of my ability the things I am.

I can lose weight and I am determined to keep trying to be successful.

Often the postponement of a desired food for one moment, one hour, will lead to a postponement for one day and miraculously postponement forever.

We have recognized the vital importance of taking just one day at a time — one pound at a time.

I cannot afford resentments — If I do I might overeat.

I will stop judging others and let God be the judge of what they do.

I realize I can't eat like my family so I provide the proper foods for myself. There is no excuse for eating the wrong kinds of foods.

I will not snack on man-made carbohydrates — sweets or starches.

Do I get up from the table as soon as a meal is over so I won't be tempted to pick leftovers?

Am I willing to change my thoughts and ideas about food and get an entirely new outlook on life?

Do you realize that your food obsession is only the outward manifestation of your inner emotional problem?

Other have had success and so can you.

Get honest with yourself now and always.

You need to read this book every day because you cannot control your eating and have very little will power.

Books of this type will give you added strength.

Don't read this book unless you have a desire to stop eating compulsively and to effect a change in your eating habits.

We have learned that praying, exercise and regular reading is essential to encourage self-discipline.

We are not saints — the point is we will keep trying. Keep changing and success will come.

Those who seek radiance bring it to those who are capable of feeling it. Discover new values and know the quality of feelings you have.

I cannot impose my will on others if the surrender of my will to God is to be effective.

I must try to think clearly and not get emotionally worked up over a problem. This keeps me from distorting the solution and excusing myself from positive actions.

I do not have to be perfect. My ideals should be high, but not out of reach. Self-doubt is wrong thinking — I must give myself credit where credit is due.

I must get over any guilt about being the person I am and take attention off myself so as to turn my attention to my problems.

People will make life worth while for me when I make life worth while for them.

Before you eat, be sure its hunger and not just desire.

Do I want to act like a baby? Putting things into my mouth that I shouldn't?

Every dull husband has a cold wife. If this is true try to help him by caring and being interested in him. This will help you both to happiness and stop your overeating.

We all have a right to happiness so we must take it — Do something to change these old patterns.

How you meet life is a matter of what you are — as a thinker and as a doer.

We must change our own bad habits before we attempt to change others.

If you are in agony and want to eat when you shouldn't — wait awhile and the impulse will go away. It may return but it will go away again. Enjoy the empty feeling. Drink some water.

No one else can change and develop my personality except me. If I believe I have the forces of truth — I have the strength of ten.

Hating someone and feeling guilty about it is about as foolish as loving someone and feeling virtuous. God made love and hate, I didn't.

I must manage myself and no one else. Most of the time people create my difficulties but it's my *attitude* toward them that depends on my reaction.

When others ignore you they may be telling you how to treat them.

Belief and positive thoughts are essential to success.

Suffering is for the purpose of arousing me; teaching me, forcing me to use my wits on the problems of my life which I can change.

One of my greatest duties in life is to act in such a way that evil forces have less and less chance to destroy my good powers of life.

My self-development and discipline are essential to serenity. I must keep my head and use my wits in an orderly manner.

Sweets and starches are an overweight person's alcohol. If I cannot eat them in moderation, I must give them up entirely.

Love alone isn't enough. It needs its mate — wisdom. Affection cannot win without understanding.

I must become more open-minded about morals and prejudices of others and myself.

I always sin when I deny myself for a purpose below my possibilities.

I must stop making the same mistakes.

If you feel hunger eat an egg or some meat. If you are still hungry, then it is only tension. Change your attitude and thinking by reading something constructive.

Exercise tones up muscles and makes you feel better. Do some daily, besides your own regular work.

Don't overeat. Do these: sew — read — phone — get out of the kitchen — sleep — go to town — work — do anything but don't eat. Drink water, coffee, tea or diet drink but don't eat. Remember this depends entirely on you. You make yourself what you are.

I will follow the best food plan for me and the one that will help me lose weight the healthiest way.

I must learn to like and accept myself so I can feel the same towards all others.

I must be happy with success and believe I deserve it. Power and accomplishment are good for me if I let it be.

How calmly, persistently and carefully I direct my thoughts determines my happiness.

I shall strive for the positive force and impelling power that will be sure to help me overcome my trouble.

As I learn to touch the hearts of others, they'll yield to my attention.

The way for me to be happier is to listen to others — feel for them and communicate with them.

I must have freedom from food. It can't manage me. I'll be indifferent to it. I'll change my attitude. It's only the first bite that really tastes good so I won't take it. The first principle is handling the situation and being independent from food so I won't have the unhappy result of guilt and weight gain.

Most fattening foods are empty calories and even a normal eater doesn't need them, so I should stop punishing myself by trying to eat a small amount of them when I really can't control myself.

Am I willing to go to any length to lose weight? Call someone, pray, read books, exercise, eat right, weigh regularly?

The ones who win are those who live without dread of being one's true self. I must dare to change my eating habits. I must construct normal ways of thinking about food and my problems will be solved.

I can ruin my life by listening to the negative opinions of others.

I will not let situations become my masters and make me turn to over-eating.

It isn't luck but belief that rules my life.

Reading self-improvement books is essential to an overeater's success for weight loss.

I must accept my responsibilities of life.

I will surrender to the good things in life. I will surrender to what I know is best for me.

People will love me for what I am. Life is full of opportunities, so I must take them when they come along.

Success begins with me, no one else.

I must gain all, but take nothing from anyone.

I must be loved by being a dynamic personality. By forgetting myself and being truly interested in what others are doing.

I must choose the right way to live for myself.

Did you know some people give up too many fats when dieting? Fats are needed in some amount for healthy hair and skin. Also fats keep you from being hungry between meals. I use safflower or corn margarine on salad dressings and fried foods.

As you become more mature in your thinking your desire for too many sweets and starches will vanish.

As you lose weight, guilt feelings of many kinds will go.

Did you ever think why you hate housework? Could it be because this is a symbol of being a woman and you would rather have been born a man?

Accepting your role and responsibility in life is one of the biggest assets to maturity.

Don't wear loose clothes, shifts or muu-muus. This encourages overeating. Wear tight fitting clothes or a belt at all times. Don't let out your belt when eating. Quit before it gets tight.

Several health books have stated that chocolate or cocoa prevent calcium assimilation. Since this is true most overweights shouldn't eat these foods which are also very high in calories.

Refined sugars are starvation foods. They satisfy our hunger and call for food, but leave our bodies deprived of proper vitamins, minerals and proteins, which we need.

Molasses — one to three tablespoons daily can make up for deficiency caused from refined sugars.

Pure white bread is not only fattening but the health thief of overeaters! All the good nutrients in wheat are taken out and given to our prize pigs and cattle; the nourishment these animals get from the wheat-germ should be ours.

In between meals try; diet drinks, frozen ice cubes of same, sugarless gum, plain coffee, tea or just plain water. If you don't like tap water keep some in the refrigerator.

If you have to eat between meals try; celery, cabbage, meat, cheese, eggs, sunflower seeds, keep within the limits of protein, vegetables and some fruits and you won't gain as much as if you eat sweets or starches.

It has been experienced by members in weight clubs that the persons who are compulsive for starches gain more rapidly and have a harder time giving them up than the ones who are strictly sweet eaters. If a person sticks to straight candy or sugar, he will not gain as rapidly on his binges as the ones who crave starches plus sweets. I am not recommending sweets.

Chocolate is one of the most craved foods of the overeater, and is the hardest one to give up. Complete abstinence from this food is the only answer. There is no such thing as a compulsive chocolate eater who can take "one bite" and stop.

We all know that carbohydrates are necessary for a good diet, *but* when a person wants to lose weight and they happen to be his binge foods he has no choice but to give them up until he reaches his goal.

Constipated? Bonnie Prudence book, "How to Keep Fit After Thirty" says that "People who move, have bowels that move." Try exercise!

If you must binge on something and you have been constipated, try eating walnuts, figs, prunes or celery.

There are some people willing to eat breakfast without toast. Are you?

Guilt is one of the biggest reasons for overeaters eating and gaining weight. The *four demons* of unhappy people are guilt, fear, inferiority feelings and hate (misguided love).

Some overeaters escape in sleep or reading, besides eating.

Lack of Vitamin B which is in whole grains can cause constipation, nervousness and fatigue. One to three tablespoons of wheatgerm can be eaten daily as it takes away all the compulsive eater's need for bread.

Do we eat to live or live to eat?

Some overweights think they should give up all fats. Don't do this. If you do, you might lose hair on your head; get dry skin; become constipated; get hungry oftener. Everyone needs at least one to two tablespoons of unsaturated fats per day. This keeps the dieter from wanting to eat between meals.

Were you told as a child any of these things, "You are too skinny, lazy, ugly, fat, too tall, no good, stupid, dumb, or short?" Any or all of these criticisms could tend to make a child grow up to be a neurotic or insecure in many ways — even overeating.

If you are a parent, don't tell your child he is "so and so and can't change it." He can be ruined by this attitude.

If you were an unhappy child, it is no wonder you are an unhappy adult. Your child from the inner past never completely leaves you, even into old age. In fact, many of our childhood anxieties are still with us and we haven't been able to mature completely.

No person is wholly mature. Even ministers and psychologists admit to some neurotic tendencies.

The only way to change a compulsive eater into a normal one

is by some kind of therapy such as books, counseling, or group therapy and clubs. Also prayer can be extremely helpful.

If you are a compulsive eater and hate to get on the scale at least once a week you are in for trouble. A possible weight gain can make you even more depressed, so keep honest and face the scale once a week, no oftener. If you are eating properly you won't need to weigh oftener.

There is no easy way to lose weight, so stop trying magic diets, pills, hypnotism, weight doctors — you alone can do it. No one thing or one person can do it for you. You must make up your mind and keep trying — no matter how many times you fail. Don't give up. "A quitter never wins and a winner never quits."

Some women crave foods at certain stress times before or during menstruation but this is no excuse or reason for giving in to their emotions. It just means we need to be that much more patient with ourselves and need more self-control. We can prepare ourselves by extra prayer and constructive reading.

Some women find that birth control pills tend to make them gain weight or feel irritable, so they must prepare themselves for extra ways to fight temptation.

Our friends who prod, tempt, or ask us to eat fattening food with them are really friendly enemies. If they truly cared about our welfare they would not insist we indulge, or tempt us.

We must improve our own lives, not others. The only person we can change is ourselves. When we change, perhaps others will see the good results and follow our pattern.

We must like ourselves and know and believe God loves us. We are forgiven for past sins. We can believe it and stop judging ourselves. No sin is too bad to forgive.

We can improve if we relax and trust in God.

As we rid ourselves of old eating habits and past frustrations we will have the strength to refuse to take them back into our lives.

We must make up our minds to take only one serving and serve our family the right kind of healthful foods. We must remove ourselves from the table and eating area as soon as possible.

When we are confronted with watching someone snack or eat fattening foods, we must, if possible, excuse ourselves and leave the area so we won't become tempted.

We shall do at least one constructive thing each day that we don't want to do. Self-discipline is one way to like ourselves.

The problems of overeating are not so simple as just staying on a diet. Selecting and preparing foods properly is necessary. Over-eaters do not apply reasonable thoughts about food. To them, it seems psychologically they enjoy food more than any other pleasure; they have very few other outlets that satisfy. If they believe only sweets and starches can satisfy their hunger, they will fight to keep them; thus fighting to hold onto their one great pleasure.

We as a nation are becoming fat but also under-nourished. We sometimes crave sweets or starches as an alcoholic craves liquor. The craving for so called "goodies" is being bred into our children the very day of birth. Instead of the life-saving colostrum from the mother's breast the baby is given sugar and water in a hospital nursery. This feeding is later changed to a formula often prepared from solids containing 50% or more refined sugar.

Later in life children are turned to refined carbohydrates because of limited food budgets, radio and television ads, tired mothers, kids' parties, Girl Scout cookies and candy — coffee breaks, teas, church functions, showers, weddings, and hundreds of other outside forces which cause a craving for sweets and starches. Whoever heard of serving raw apples or oranges, nuts, vegetables, meats at a social function? It would be laughed at! The compulsive eater is brainwashed to believe he needs these foods and doesn't want to give them up willingly.

We have tried desperately to stop overeating. We were filled with the illusion that we could someday eat like normal people if we wanted to. We tried time and time again to diet and give up fattening foods but we could not do either. We always lapsed into ceaseless, unhappy eating habits.

Wives, husbands, families, friends and employers threw up their hands in disgust, bewilderment and despair. They stopped mentioning the subject, so we kept gaining weight. We wanted to stop overeating. We realized that our overeating was a crazy excuse. Now we can use this book to help give up excuses or reasons and get a better eating plan and better daily living schedule so that we can begin to get control of ourselves in every respect.

Let us not be afraid to reveal our real feelings about life and to share them with someone so we can help ourselves. Let our fears of being rejected or criticized not keep us from getting counseling.

Everyone needs help; no one is strong unto himself. Let us be great enough to be humble and willing to seek help. Let us be honest with ourselves and our needs and be willing to work at it.

If we want to be miserable, we can continue overeating, thinking about ourselves and how much food we need, how hungry we are, how sorry we are for ourselves and how we wish someone would help us.

If we want to be happy, we can get the courage to quit overeating. Think about others and do something for them. We can forget about food and our obsession for it. We can count our blessings and thank God we have a disease that is curable.

We will face our daily lives with pleasure; to choose the right foods and accept our lives as they come — Fitting ourselves to each situation without turning to food.

We will accept the things about others and situations that we cannot change and hope to have the wisdom to know the difference.

Is your church and spiritual life helping your eating problems? Why not? Are you in the religion of your choice or someone else's choice? Seek out the best one for your needs.

Don't throw away any clothes that are too small or tight. This is a defeatist attitude. Hang one out where you can constantly see it to remind you that you can get to that size again. Face your true self 'till you are ready to give up overeating.

We think we can control our eating, but sometimes our unconscious makes us want to eat compulsively because something is bothering us.

If you get out into the open with someone you can trust the things that really bother you can be controlled.

Give yourself a pep talk on how to really feel and think — be willing to change.

Are you really in control of your actions or are the past fears, doubts, etc. controlling them?

If you face your dilemma and be honest, then you can start to really live.

If you are a man, do you want to be a man? If you are a woman, do you really want to be a woman? Play the role you are and enjoy it.

People who cannot like themselves cannot like anyone else.

Is the anxiety in your life preventing you from loving others? Do you have unreal fears of past and future? Hatred in life is usually due to fear. Know it and live it; admit it, then you can give it up when you no longer feel the need for it.

Are you physically and emotionally an adult, but still acting like a child?

Take time to think of all the good things about yourself, your life, your relatives. Positive thoughts bring positive feelings and actions.

Be glad your alive — you are a very important person.

Is your reaction to life either "good" or "bad"? Try to be moderate in your thinking.

Don't feel you have to be like someone else. Be yourself even if someone wants you to be otherwise.

Do I realize that there is a God who cares for me and am I willing to pour out my cares to Him in earnest satisfying prayer? Am I sure that He really listens or do I think He doesn't? If I do believe why don't I seek Him more often?

I realize that God's love is best mediated through persons; that is why I must seek out the help from those who believe in God and those whom God has helped. Let me keep trying and never give up.

Self-rejection: Loneliness is the overeater's alienation from God, from himself and from his fellow man. Many of these feelings are not our fault. We were raised in that type of environment.

Sin is rejecting God — sin is seeking to escape from ourselves. Sometimes our families can't help us so we must relate to others who judge us less harshly.

We cannot love people until we know them. We cannot feel hate until we first have felt love. Love and hate are so close. When someone whom we love hurts us we sometimes feel hate towards them and then feel guilty.

Don't be afraid to cry once in awhile. It does magic for the soul at times. That's what tears are for — to cry.

Are you overprotecting yourself from some of life's experiences? Experience any experience and live it to the fullest — good or bad — live it you must.

Don't ask yourself, "Are my actions or overeating good or bad?" but, "do I act the way I really want to act and am I eating what I really want to eat? Do I have a purpose for my life?"

You must realize you are a worthy person and stop feeling guilty, friendless, self-pity, hate and fear. Act happy and you will get happy.

Stop punishing yourself by overeating. Do something constructive about your faults.

How you lost your weight is how you'll probably have to eat the rest of your life. What you do while you are losing is what you will do the rest of your life.

There are Three kinds of people;

A few who make things happen,

Many who watch things happen,

An overwhelming number who have no idea that anything is happening.
Which *kind* are you?

ESPECIALLY FOR OVERWEIGHT TEENAGERS

I worked for two years with a girls' weight-losing group. There were a few success stories I could tell, but most of the girls had no lasting success because they didn't get any help at home, they didn't come to meetings regularly, or because they were emotionally unstable. Many of them came from broken homes or had some other emotional problem. These girls were in need of love and understanding. Most of them hated themselves and felt unworthy of being alive.

They blamed themselves for their misfortune and this brought on guilt feelings. Some of them would cheat and tell their parents that they came to meetings when they went downtown instead. They didn't want to stop eating, but they wanted to lose weight. Most of these girls had beautiful faces and would be very attractive if they reached their normal weight. I would get upset when I tried so hard to help them, and got very little cooperation from their parents. Sometimes a parent of a girl was also fat, and so did very little to help her daughter lose weight. Someday I hope the parents, school officials, and doctors will care enough about the overweight teenager to do something to really help them.

*   *   *

Do you blame your parents for your overweight? Perhaps you think it is their fault, but even if it is, you are old enough now to decide whether you are going to continue in this pattern of overeating the wrong foods.

Perhaps as a baby some adults bribed you with foods such as candy, ice cream, or cookies, so you'd stop crying or be good or do something you didn't want to do. They made a "big thing" of eating, so that it became too important in your life.

This may have given you a means of satisfying your body at the time, but it was probably not food that you needed, but love and understanding. Sometimes you may have even sneaked these "goodies" to eat when you could not cope with a situation or when you were bored. You were using food as an alcoholic uses liquor or a smoker uses cigarettes. These are all oral satisfaction compulsions which can ruin one's life if they get uncontrollable. They can ruin your life not only physically but emotionally and spiritually as well.

Physically, they can ruin your good health and bring on a great number of diseases. Emotionally, they can ruin your life because they keep you from doing something more constructive and they make you crave more and more until you have no control over yourself. Spiritually they can ruin your life because they will give you guilt feelings and keep you from knowing a loving God who cares for you. They can keep you from praying because you will feel unworthy of God's love while you indulge in these compulsions.

Overeating has become a habit and it is up to you whether you continue this compulsion or not. You have set up a habit of snacking but don't think for one minute that this habit has to continue as you grow into adulthood. It doesn't, unless you want it to. Your parents set patterns of thinking for you up to the age of 6 and from then on you set your own.

It is your attitude about food and overeating which will help you get trim or stay fat. It is up to you and it's your decision to leave certain foods alone. No one can do it for you. There is no magic formula. First, you can face your nude body in a full length mirror. If you don't have one at home, go into a department store dressing room and take an honest look at yourself. Decide how much weight you need to lose and make a vow right then and there to lose it.

After deciding how much weight you want to lose, try to find out why you crave certain foods. Is it self-pity, resentment, hate, inferiority, fear, guilt, boredom, feeling unloved, or something else? Try to look at the reasons and decide which ones you can change and how you can go about doing it.

Be sure to give yourself credit for the good things about your body that are attractive. Name them. Give yourself credit for the good qualities of your personality. Remember that God gave you your looks, but your personality is your own choice. Accept yourself with all of your weaknesses and try to strengthen the ones that you know you can improve. Hold your head up high, and believe you were put on this earth for a specific purpose and you are going to fulfill it.

Try to find another teenager who is also overweight. Work with that person. Misery loves company and besides helping yourself, you will be helping her too. This is a good way to make yourself feel more important. We always like ourselves better when we share experiences which are meaningful to us.

Join a weight group if you can, but be sure it helps you. If you don't start losing weight and keep it off, something may be wrong with the club, or you aren't ready to give up compulsive eating.

Even if you have been told by others you are bad, lazy, no good, dirty, dumb, or many other insults, that doesn't mean it is true. You don't have to be any of these things. You have the power to be the person you want to become. It will take a lot of determination and work on your part, but you can succeed. Have faith in yourself even if it seems that no one else does. Just because someone tears you down, doesn't mean you have to sit around feeling sorry for yourself. You should be that much more determined to show yourself and others that you can succeed.

It is an art to accept criticism and learn from it. If it is constructive criticism it usually comes from one who loves you and is really concerned about you. Sometimes criticism from a parent or other member of the family or a relative sounds cruel, but usually a person does not criticize another unless he has some true feelings for that person. Criticism usually stems from the fact that the other person sees his faults in you or that he is jealous. If you remember this, criticism will be easier to accept.

Resentment is one of the biggest reasons teenagers eat when they shouldn't. They don't know how to cope with it. This is where prayer comes in handy. I know many young people don't believe there is a loving God who cares for them, but if they turn to prayer, they soon find peace and understanding within themselves. All people need a Higher Power greater than themselves because there are so many times in our lives when we desperately need help. If you are eating compulsively, you need a Higher Power. Search for it. There is no one person who has the same kind of faith as another. We are all individuals so you must find the kind of faith that will best suit your needs.

Becoming angry or afraid is another reason teenagers overeat or turn to too many sweets and starches. They are searching for an answer. They can't find it, so they eat. Try to find an outlet of some kind besides food. Try taking a run down the road, get out of the house, exercise, read a book, look at TV. You can play a game, draw, play a musical instrument or anything else, but don't eat compulsively because it will make things worse.

As you begin to stay on a proper diet, you will begin to like yourself more each day. You will feel glad to be alive, be worthy of doing many things and be happier with others. Liking and accepting yourself is the biggest job in your life. These two things are vital to your success in weight loss and your whole future. Be good to yourself; keep yourself and your room neat because you want to, not because your parents say you have to. Don't be your own worst enemy. You don't want to grow up to be a cranky old adult, do you? Live well in the present and dream about the future. Forget the past. You can do anything that is worth doing.

Even though your parents have control of many of your actions, you are really in charge of what you want to become. If they want your future to be something that you do not want, try to get some help from a teacher, minister, or another mature adult who can talk with you and your parents in order to get some satisfactory solution. Many times parents are right in knowing what's best for a child but also many times someone on the outside can open their thoughts to your views. Your life is your own to live as an adult the way you see fit. It is your responsibility to your true self to seek guidance for your future.

Don't let any parent or relative make you believe that you have to be fat because they say it is heredity. *Fat is not inherited.* It is only the appetites and eating habits that we get that seem to give this impression. If your family has poor eating habits, it makes it hard to change them, but it can be accomplished with a little cooperation from the cook. Explain to her that fattening foods are not especially good for even thin, normal people. Excess refined carbohydrates are harmful to the health of anyone. They can also cause many cavities if your teeth are not brushed within 20 minutes after eating. That is one reason alone for not snacking on sweets between meals. Your family will admire you if you take an interest in health and nutrition and this will help you to have a happier family relationship.

You will begin to get a feeling of satisfaction from your new disciplined life. The more you practice, the easier it will become. Try getting up early and doing 15 minutes of strenuous exercise before breakfast. Eat a good breakfast of protein, fruit, and milk. Stay away from the fattening starches and sweets. You don't have to starve to lose weight. Get your own breakfast if your cook refuses to give you the proper foods.

You can cook some boiled eggs while you are getting dressed. It only takes a few minutes to prepare a healthful meal and your body deserves the best.

Ask the cook or the person who shops in your family to have plenty of non-fattening foods available, if you do have to go on a binge. Celery, lettuce, and dill pickles are good chewing foods. Try to stay on three meals a day because that is a wonderful self-discipline, but be sure you eat enough of the proper foods so you won't be hungry between meals. Don't give up too many fats. Fats of corn oil or safflower are the best for dieters. Fats keep you from being hungry and you need them for a healthy body.

Do you have a habit of biting your nails, swearing, smoking, or anything else that you dislike in yourself? If so, try working on that also. These habits brought some kind of satisfaction to you at one time or another. Outwardly you act as if you don't care, but inwardly you wish you could stop. Ask yourself if you are getting the satisfaction that you want from this habit. Try to find out if there is not some better way of securing satisfaction. Then you can make progress in breaking the habit.

Our feelings and emotions make us what we are. When we are at war with others, we have no peace in ourselves. When we hate others, we cannot like ourselves. When we make others miserable, we are unhappy ourselves.

Get some of your overweight friends to take their lunches to school so you can eat together and not be tempted by the snack bar, candy machines, or high calorie cafeteria lunches. It is difficult for teenagers to keep away from these temptations because most students eat them.

Remember that you are not a normal eater but a compulsive overeater who needs to lose weight. Your body cannot "afford" refined carbohydrates.

Start your own self-improvement club with other interested students. Be honest with yourself by keeping a chart of everything you eat. Write them down *before* you eat them. Weigh yourself just once a week because if you are honest with your eating you will lose weight. Let God be your Higher Power instead of food and your scales. Sometimes dieters get on the scales to see how much they got by with. They may be tempted to eat a lot if they have lost more than they expected. Be sure to tell yourself that you deserve success. Some overeaters feel so unworthy that when they lose weight they eat and gain it back because subconsciously they don't feel they really deserve the best.

Sometimes you may be frightened about something, and then you eat because you feel ashamed of yourself for being afraid. Most adults have fears of some kind. Just because a person grows up is no proof that he is mature. Remember not to judge yourself too harshly for fears that are normal. You are brave in other ways and we are all individuals.

The greatest desire of any child, teenager, or adult is to be loved. We want the friendly, affectionate response of others and we want them to care for us and accept us as we are. We want to be liked by parents, brothers, sisters, and friends. Sometimes we act as if we don't care, but deep down inside we do. We sometimes cover up our greatest desires because we don't feel worthy of this kind of love. That is why some teenagers overeat. So the first step to recovery from compulsive eating is to love yourself properly. Maybe no one else will and it is your duty to yourself.

Try to experience any kind of new thing that may come into your life as long as your conscience tells you that it can be meaningful. Don't avoid going places just because you are fat. Be happy and act as if you are enjoying yourself and people will like you in spite of your size. Don't pretend you would rather stay home when you don't want to. Be brave and live while you are young. There may come a time later in your life for sitting home when you wish you could go out.

Don't blame your parents or someone else for your failures. They do not manage your life as much as you sometimes think. You may continue overeating if you keep blaming others for your failures. This is only an escape from facing the real problems of how you can change if you really want to better your life.

Boys and men hate to see or hear a girl or woman cry. Most men have absolutely no pity or concern for the female who cries. They try to escape from the situation. Tears help a female, but they do no good for a male because he is taught from early childhood that "big boys don't cry." If you girls have to cry, go to another female and do it or go in your room in private and have a good cry. It may release your emotions so you won't have to eat.

If life denies you some of the things you want, you can still be happy. Of course you can — on one condition, namely, that you are honest with yourself. Decide exactly what you want out of life. You may have to live your life partly with second best but don't try to blame it on anyone else. You may find certain pathways in life closed, but others will be open for you. Keep on searching and you will find a solution.

Teenagers and all people are basically selfish. You were born that way. But as life goes on, you will find that true happiness comes from thinking of others as well as yourself. The more you help someone else, the more happiness you will find.

Teenagers can save themselves many heartaches if they try to understand that most parents are having a terrible struggle in their own lives. They, too have their doubts, fears, nervous habits, sorrows and a feeling of unworthiness. Most parents do the best they can as they bring up their children. It may not appear to be so, but I believe that this is true. No parent knowingly wants to hurt his offspring. Some parents have been hurt so much by their own past that they cannot show love to their children. Teenagers would have more understanding of their parent's actions and words if they realized this. It is a shock for a child when he first learns that his parents are not perfect.

If you compulsive overeating teenagers are carrying resentment toward one or both parents or some other person, this is the time to get rid of it by forgiving that person and then forgiving yourself for having that resentment. Until you do, you will be tempted to turn to food for consolation. You can change your whole attitude toward the situation which is past. You cannot change the fact that it happened, but you can accept the fact that it did happen and stop letting the past hurt you.

You may be the only child in the family. Perhaps you were spoiled and given too many "goodies" because your parents didn't know how to show love in any way except by giving you treats and luxuries. You may have gotten an overdose of too much attention and possessive love from other adults. It is usually unhealthy for an only child to be with adults constantly, because he is apt to take life too seriously. A child needs to have fun with playmates his own age. Self-discipline from compulsive overeating has to be learned by the spoiled child the hard way. Life's experiences sometimes are hard to take but they can help you to grow into a mature adult if you accept them for what they are worth.

Perhaps you were a sickly child and your parents wanted to build up your strength, so they gave you fattening foods, thinking they would help you. They may have pampered you too much and you began to enjoy all the extra attention, so you ate to keep their love.

Maybe you were the baby in the family and were resented by your older brothers and sisters, or even felt unwanted by one of your parents. This could be the cause of your turning to food for comfort.

Perhaps you are the oldest child and too many responsibilities were put upon you. You were treated as an adult and expected to act like one too soon. You turned to food because you felt so many burdens put upon your shoulders.

Perhaps your parents were divorced or one of them died. This form of insecurity could cause a child or teenager to turn to food for solace.

Lack of complete understanding and affection between parents can cause you to feel mixed emotions and if there seems to be no solution, you might be turning to foods because you feel so helpless. You love both parents but when they are fighting, your sense of security is shaken. Now is the time to tell yourself, "Perhaps they are having problems, but I don't have to 'eat about it.' "

Sometimes parents try to hold the family ties so close that you feel bound by their apron strings and are not able to think for yourself or make your own decisions about life. It is hard for a teenager to go against his own parent's will, but after you get worthwhile advice, sometimes this becomes necessary for all concerned. You have to do your own thinking and your own living the way you believe that God wants you to. When you rebel, be sure you don't go to extremes and hurt your parents just because you feel they have hurt you. Remember they do not purposely want to make you overly dependent on them.

Sometimes teenagers break away from home too soon; then guilt feelings come which could very easily turn them into compulsive eaters, alcoholics, or drug addicts. They leave the security of the home which they resented, but later find that home was much better than any other place they have found. You must stand on your own two feet, but be sure that you are ready when you go. Most parents will keep loving you no matter how you live your life. The most important thing for you to remember is to keep your own self-worth and like yourself. Be worthy of being a human being so you don't have to turn to any kind of compulsive habit for escape.

If you want to get rid of excess weight, there are many things that you can do to help. First try to find a special interest in something besides food. When you are busy with other activities, your desire to eat will become less. You will like yourself, and others will like you, because your life will be more interesting. Try to be with other people who are naturally happy. Be interested in what other people do. If you are at a social gathering and feel left out of things, look around the room and find someone who is also alone. Be a friend and soon you will have friends.

Sometimes you don't get good grades in school and that may make you feel inferior, so you may eat for comfort. If you do your best, you have no reason to have guilt feelings. Sometimes parents make the mistake of comparing you with one of your classmates or relatives. You don't have to let this turn you to food either. Either accept it or do something to better the situation. Your future happiness does not depend upon the exact grades you get in school, but the amount of self-discipline and the quality of your work. Try to find out what you are best suited for in life, and go after it with all the ambition and interest you have. Emotional family problems sometimes keep a teenager from doing the best he can in school, so you must learn to leave these problems at home and concentrate on your education which will lead you to more happiness.

Sometimes guilt feelings about sex tend to make a teenager turn to food. Be sure that what you think and do are not wrong. Perhaps you have been told certain things are sinful by some unknowing adult, but you can find out exactly what is good or bad if you read many good books which are especially written for the teenager's sex education.

Even if you have had an experience with sex which makes you feel guilty, it doesn't mean that you have to spend the rest of your life punishing yourself by overeating. Any sin can be forgiven. Be sure you forgive yourself. You know God has. Love must be real in order for a teenager to measure his true feelings. Playing a game with bodies can lead to disastrous results. There are many ways to show love besides the physical acts.

Teenagers can swim, dance, go to the movies, skate, sing, attend church, or many other enjoyable activities. Be sure you are emotionally mature before you decide to get married. Some teenagers get married just to get away from home or they get married for security. An unhappy marriage can make a compulsive eater out of either wife or husband in a short time.

Too often religion does not play an important part in a teenager's life. Some young people shy away from religion because they were forced to go to Sunday School or church when they didn't want to, or because they don't feel it helps their lives. Perhaps this is the time to visit other churches of different religions or faiths. There may be one more suited to your needs than the one your ancestors have handed down to you. You will have a fuller and more meaningful life if you can find a faith which is a living one. If you try to find what God has intended for you to be and do, you will have the joy and satisfaction of achieving more than you ever dreamed possible. Seek out people whom you greatly admire and ask them about their spiritual beliefs. This can strengthen your own faith and give you the will to stand any trials and tribulations that have to be experienced. Everyone needs something to depend on and God is the best choice. He is also the safest one to depend on. He will never let you down, where people sometimes do. A faith in a living God can hold you steady in the midst of all difficulties. He does not save us from all pain and suffering, but He can help us accept or rise above them. Remember you are worthy of God's love no matter what your past is. You can live a worthwhile life and *give up compulsive overeating.*

DENTAL DECAY, DIET, AND REFINED CARBOHYDRATES

(Quote, taken from an Agricultural Extension Service Bulletin)

"A balanced diet and good oral hygiene habits can prevent dental decay, the nation's most prevalent disease, according to E. Charles Watkins, Associate Clinical Professor of Operative Dentistry at the University of California Medical Center here. Americans are getting cavities at such a rate that if the country's dentists worked 24 hours a day for the next year, they would be further behind at the end of the year than when they started. Too many think the situation is hopeless, but dental disease can be prevented or controlled in 95% of all cases by common sense habits of oral hygiene and good diet. Dr. Watkins emphasized that teeth should be brushed as soon as possible after every meal. He says to concentrate on the gumline which is the area where dental accumulation collects and decay thrives. Brushing can halt a gum line cavity that may be beginning if decay hasn't broken the enamel. Dental floss and toothpicks help prevent dental disease because they reach where a toothbrush can't. Brushing should start at the age of one and a half years to give the child a head start on cavity prevention. A child should take care of his baby teeth since they maintain the space in the dental arch for the permanent teeth. The *carbohydrate* diet which comes with our high standards of living is the source of most dental problems. The villains are sugar and sugar-forming starches which stick to the teeth and provide the environment for tooth decay. These soft foods do not give enough stimulation to the gums; coarser foods such as carrots, celery, and apples are better for the teeth because they clean as they are eaten."

*   *   *

The above statements are a joy to my heart, because they tell exactly the way I feel about refined carbohydrates. This is one reason I am writing this book. Our children and adults in America are not only eating too many refined sweets and starches at meals, but worst of all, they are eating them in between meals without even brushing their teeth. This reason alone is enough for us to give them up entirely.

Think of the times when special so called "goodies" (really they should be called "baddies") are eaten by both adults and children. At the age when a child is still in the buggy or stroller he is handed a candy sucker by a well meaning storekeeper. Candy is given out by Santa Claus at Christmas time when large amounts are eaten with no tooth brushing. Popsicles, gum and other sweets are consumed by thousands of Americans which are detrimental to not only their teeth but their health as well. Candy between meals can cut down children's appetite for more healthful foods. Adults and children both are always fed refined carbohydrates for refreshments after parties where they have no chance to brush their teeth. Tooth decay can set in after 20 minutes of contacting the teeth. We bring home treats of these fattening foods for our children because they have been "good" or to bribe them in some way, or to show our love. What kind of love is it to give our children cavities? Very few people think they can go to the movies or an entertainment of any other kind without eating some kind of refined carbohydrates.

I hope that this chapter will wake up many conscientious parents, who really love their children. They can help educate their own children about tooth decay and the damage of refined carbohydrates for the body. This can be done at a very early age, and the sooner the better. Snacks such as apples can be taken to the movies. Other kinds of foods can also be served at parties or club meetings. It is just such an old custom that we think we have to keep up this serving of refined carbohydrates. If a person eats three nourishing meals a day there is no real need for "snacking" of any kind.

CONFESSIONS FROM VARIOUS SNEAK EATERS

I used to hide a jar of peanut butter so no one would find it and know how much I ate.

I used to lock the kids out of the house so I could eat and they wouldn't see me.

I went to P.T.A. and didn't take any refreshments but when I got home I went on a terrible binge and ate more than I would have eaten there.

I was cooking a roast for dinner and by the time I served it I realized that I had eaten half of it. I hoped my family hadn't noticed how small it was.

I was frying chicken and when I served it the kids asked me why it only had one leg, one wing, and no neck.

I was making cup cakes and the recipe said that it was supposed to make two dozen. By the time I got the batter ready for the oven, there was only half that amount left to bake.

I have eaten one dozen doughnuts in one day.

I made a lemon pie for my family but ate the whole thing myself so I had to quickly make them another one before they discovered it.

I always bought the kids Easter candy a week in advance and sometimes I would have to go out and buy the same amount over again because I had eaten it all.

I used to wait till the children were in bed so I could take the best trick-or-treat candy for myself.

When I have company I eat very little. But after they leave I go on a binge.

When I fed the baby in the high-chair I always felt that I had to taste the food. I would give the baby a bite, then I would take a bite.

I hid candy in my bedroom and would go in and eat it in private.

As soon as the night meal was over, I would eat up all the left-overs as I did the dishes.

I once bought myself a whole loaf of French bread and a whole pound of butter. I ate all of it myself.

I used to eat candy bars in bed but I had to be careful so my husband couldn't hear the rattling of the wrapper.

I used to sit on a reducing vibrating machine but how was I supposed to lose weight while I was eating a piece of fruit cake at the same time?

I wouldn't eat at a birthday party, but when I came home I ate 10 popcorn balls in private.

I was hostess at a party so I felt I had to keep busy in the kitchen while the guests played games. I would keep snacking on the refreshments but not eat any when I served them.

I started on a diet and decided to give up candy, but I ate all kinds of other sweets instead.

I gave up sweets for Lent but as soon as Lent was over I made up for what I had given up.

If there is only one pastry or a piece of some dessert left over from the family meal, I would hide it and eat it later myself.

I used to buy more than a dozen of anything at the bakery so my family wouldn't know that I had eaten any.

When I couldn't sleep at night I used to eat.

When I was pregnant I ate for two. When I was nursing the baby I still ate for two.

I always bought candy because it was on sale and it was a good buy.

I ate the crusts and leftovers from my children's plates because I hated to see them go to waste. They went to my waist!

I'd keep my ice cream dish in the refrigerator so it would keep cold for my next serving.

We were given candy at Christmas so I had to have my share. I used to poke them and eat only the chewy ones, leaving the rest.

I am a garbage eater. I used to eat all the leftovers — now I put them down the disposal.

One morning, on our ranch I had fixed myself a big breakfast; 4 sausages, a large bowl of hot cereal, 4 eggs, and 5 pieces of toast. I was almost ready to sit down and eat them when my husband came in from the barn. I quickly hid them in the cupboard because I was so ashamed of the amount, but I still intended to eat them 'though I had to wait 'till he left. I wanted him to go back outside, so I picked a fight with him so he would get mad and leave me alone so I could eat in private.

I sometimes bought a round coffee cake and would always cut it in half, so I could take an even amount of pieces from the middle and then push the two pieces left together, so no one could tell how much I ate.

EMOTIONS AND THE COMPULSIVE OVEREATER

(Taken by the author at several public lectures by a well known counselor and minister who wishes to remain anonymous since he has terminated his public lectures after many years.)

*   *   *

Some people believe that mental problems (neurosis) gradually get worse and become psychotic. Some believe neurotic neurosis is from brain damage. All of us are subject to some neurosis. Even doctors, ministers, psychiatrists and other professional people have some neuroses. There is no completely whole mature person. We are not perfectly adjusted all the time. The more we talk and relate to others the more we agree. That is why a compulsive overeater can get help by group therapy. He finds out that there are many others who have the craving for some sweet or starch at all times, and even if they realize that these foods will make them gain weight, their emotions are so strong that they will give in to them and eat. Good mental health or emotional stability is wanted by all of us. We constantly seek ways to help ourselves to a happier life. A mature person is one who has the ability to fulfill his functions with a fair degree of happiness. When we are stuffing extra food into our mouths we are not functioning constructively and we are certainly not happy.

Some people think their physical symptoms are their problems but they are not. Our feelings and emotions about life are the cause of our physical problems, whether it be overeating and weight, headaches, biting nails, smoking, drinking, taking drugs, or many other physical escapes.

Only recently we have begun to study ourselves and know the reasons for our behavior. Personality adjustment is necessary before an overweight person can lose weight and keep it off. Thousands have gone to weight and regular doctors and lost hundreds of pounds. One lady and many others have lost 75 pounds several times but sooner or later gain it all back, plus a few more. This is because she and the others were treating the symptom instead of the real problem which she found out later. A test she took in our group showed that she had 99% inferiority feelings. Anyone with that high a score has to go into deep therapy if she wishes to get completely well from compulsive overeating. This usually stems from early childhood experiences. There are many steps one can take for help. One is to get direct counseling from a competent person. It could be professional, or some person who himself has "arrested" the "disease" of compulsive eating. Our subconscious plays a large part in our actions and emotions. Our conscious tells us not to eat fattening foods, but our unconscious tells us to go ahead because this food tastes so good. Our selfconscious tells us what to do, what we want, what is proper, but when we get out of our proper actions and place we get into trouble. Man is in conflict mostly with the realm of the subconscious. On the surface we pay the price by gaining weight, we are not happy, can't make decisions and frustrations follow. We don't have to understand our subconscious, to realize our wrong way of living and overeating.

Some try to interpret their dreams, but it is very difficult and technical. Dreams are hard to remember and unless we have professional help we may interpret them wrong. If we dream the same dream over and over, it is a good idea to look into the meaning of it if we can.

A counselor usually doesn't give direct advice to a client. He is a reflector of troubled persons. He relates to the client because he understands feelings. A good counselor will be able to get his client to tell all his troubles. Little by little the overeater can find his way out just by the counselor's listening. For every overeater there is a cause for his overeating and weight gain. There is no one who overeats and is fat because he wants to be or just because he likes food. I've heard this from many newcomers in my groups. After they have attended a few meetings, they find out some of the real reasons for their problems. Don't kid yourself into thinking you are overweight just because you like to eat. Of course that is one reason, but the main reason is probably in your subconscious mind. Just face the fact that you have an eating problem which probably stems from your past, or from present experiences. Now that you are willing to get control of your overeating you can become mature in other ways as well. It will take time and effort on your part, but if you have enough faith it can be done.

To locate the cause of overeating sometimes takes time. There are no short cuts. It took a long time for you to get this way, and it may take you a while to get better. But remember, it is worth all the time and effort you can give to it. The old habits of snacking and "bingeing" can be unlearned. Practice it every day. Just three small meals a day and no in-between meal snacks. There are no magic formulas or short cuts for losing weight. It means determination and hard work and mental alertness. When you feel yourself getting emotionally upset by something don't try to escape by overeating. The situation or problem will still be there after you have eaten and then you will have added an extra problem of a weight gain.

Many deal with overweight by taking diet pills, tranquilizers, and other drugs. These help only temporarily. We can be cured by talking things out with someone who cares. When tempted to eat, get on the phone and call someone who is a pleasant person and who will help you to get a better outlook on your situation. Or get in the car and go visit someone who is worse off than you. Sometimes just doing some kind of action such as pulling weeds, scrubbing floors, or even reading, helps.

Every individual feels: 1 — toward people; 2 — against people; 3 — away from people. These are normal feelings. Sometimes we compulsive overeaters get guilt feelings when we have these perfectly normal feelings that everyone has. We must learn to accept our feelings without blaming ourselves for them. Guilt is one of the biggest reasons for overeating.

Repression is the pushing back of something which we suspect in ourselves as wrong. We can forget the unpleasant things about ourselves, but if we dig them up and face them, we can accept them. If we put these things back into the subconscious they will appear in compulsive eating or headaches or some other symptom.

Rationalizing is not reasoning even if we think it is. It is only to justify what we want to do, or where we want to go, or what we want to say. We may think that we need refined carbohydrates, but when our body tells us we eat too many or we can't control the amount, it is time to "get honest with ourselves." Let us admit that there are some people who can eat these fattening foods and not gain weight, but don't think for one split second that we are normal eaters because we know from bitter experience that we are not. Perhaps someday when we get our thinking straight, we can eat normally but until we feel mentally mature, let us not fool around testing our compulsive personalities.

Sometimes we compulsive overeaters compensate for our shortcomings by being compulsive talkers. We have to use our mouths. If we aren't eating we think we have to talk. We blame our eating on others. We blame our weakness and faults on situations.

Sometimes we overeaters are also perfectionists. We labor to get certain things done exactly right to cover up for the things we don't do that we know we should. This outward perfection covers up our own imperfection. If this is overdone the subconscious is aware that we need to correct some inside things.

When something is very wrong and an overeater won't face or attack the person or problem he sooner or later turns to food for release. This can be dangerous because if we dwell on negative thoughts too long our minds will become bitter and our eating will continue and we will not only gain weight but be a mess in general. There are two steps which the alcoholic can take to get "well". One is, "list all the persons he had harmed, and become willing to make amends to them all". The other one is "make direct amends to such people wherever possible, except when to do so would injure them or others". These two steps seem hard for us to do. And they are. But the ones who have taken these steps succeeded in getting rid of their compulsions.

An honest desire to know our inner self is the solution to compulsive eating. There are many good things in all of us and some bad ones. We seem to remember the bad ones more than the good ones. We must attack our inner-selves often and make some progress daily. Sometimes it is painful, but persistent study of our inner life will help us to recovery. It takes time but it is worth it.

Sometimes we idealize ourselves too much or we tear ourselves down too much. We must try to study our motives and face the true self. What are our motives for doing something? Obligation? Being kind? Sacrificing? Publicity? Hard work? Money? Friendship? All of these are reasons why we do certain things in life. I am writing this book because I feel an *obligation* to help others. I am *being kind* by sharing my experiences with my readers. I am *sacrificing* time from my family duties to write it. I will get *publicity* which will make me feel more worthy as a person. I am a *hard worker* and selling this book will bring me *money*. It will bring me *friends* also. There is no one special reason for my writing it. All these reasons will help me to become a better person.

We must pay attention to criticism from others. Especially if it comes from several different sources. Don't resent it. Maybe the criticism is valid. Take it for what you can learn from it, and then dismiss it from your mind. After we find out our faults we can accept them, but we don't have to approve of them. In fact the next step is to try to change them. Feeling unwanted or unloved as a child can be reasons for our overeating now, but this does not have to continue.

If we look at them objectively and talk to someone about them, we can learn to be patient and get help to overcome our frustrations. We can be free from emotions that we don't want because there is a drive in all of us to try and to keep on trying. So don't give up!

MOST OVERWEIGHT MARRIED PEOPLE DON'T ENJOY SEX

If a husband wants his wife to enjoy sex, he should remember that a woman has a different outlook on sex than a man. She wants to be shown love and affection during the day as well as in bed. She wants to be wanted by her husband just because he cares for her as a person. When a woman feels disapproval from her husband in any area, she feels unloved. If he criticizes her body in any way, especially her fat, she feels unworthy of being loved by him.

She wants him to dominate her, but do it in a loving way. If he can say, "Honey, I love you so much. Please stop overeating so you and I can be happier," she is likely to do something about her weight if she feels he really cares and is not just criticizing. If he calls her a "pig" or tells her to "grow up", or tells her to "use a little will power," it does absolutely no good and may make her go eat more when he isn't around.

An overweight woman needs constructive help. She needs the security of knowing others accept her as she is. A wife who is a compulsive eater often feels ashamed to be loved because of her fat body. She sometimes does not permit herself to accept love even when it is given. Guilt feelings arise from her compulsive eating.

This becomes a menace to a wife's sex life. She knows her faults, but doesn't have the power to change. When she does get the courage to diet, she likes herself more and is more loving not only to her husband, but to her family and friends.

The wife and mother is the main "cog" in the wheel. It is her actions, moods, and feelings that set the whole emotional pattern for a successful marriage. If a husband wants his wife to lose weight and be loving, he should insist that she get proper counseling from the right source. Dieting and losing weight are not enough to help a woman to enjoy sex. The man is the head of the household and even if she fights him on this decision to get help, she will be happier in the long run. She will then realize how much he really loves her. Of course he should be willing to go along with the counseling himself since he too can improve in the areas needed.

This does not mean having to pay large amounts of money for counseling. There are many qualified ministers who can help greatly, besides many wonderful books which can guide the couple to a better sexual relationship.

Some people feel that marriage should be on a "fifty-fifty" basis, but I believe the wife has to change first. She has more responsibility and opportunity to make a happy home. This doesn't sound fair to women, but it is true nevertheless. A man will usually change when he sees that his wife is willing to go all the way to help make him happy sexually.

If a domineering woman marries a passive man, she is apt to become too dominant herself, thus causing even more frustrations, because deep inside she really does not want to play the dominant role. Counseling and reading books on love can bring about a better relationship. If a man is too dominant, his wife fears him and this keeps her from loving him. She cannot enjoy sex. She might even sneak food and overeat because she feels he doesn't understand her needs.

Communication is necessary for a happy home life. Being able to "talk things out" on any subject is essential. There are topics such as; sex, death, wills, religion, politics, fears, desires, finances, and many others which should not be avoided, but discussed openly and calmly. Understanding each other's feelings on different matters brings about a better relationship. If this becomes impossible between husband and wife, outside counseling is advisable.

Sex to a woman should be just as enjoyable as it is to a man. She should try to forget the cares of the day and concentrate on the subject at hand. To make her husband happy is the most important job she has and his needs should not be neglected because of her preoccupation with the cares of her children and other matters. Some day her children will be out of the household and she should strive to keep a wholesome relationship with her husband so they can continue a meaningful life together.

Just because a wife married her man doesn't mean she can neglect all the little things that helped attract him in the first place. Sometimes when a woman is overweight she might feel there is no use in trying to be attractive. She should not give up. She can keep clean. She can wear her hair as attractively as possible, buy the most flattering clothes and nightwear. She should smell sweet at all times and look as feminine and attractive as she can, not only for her husband, but for herself.

Some women admit they would rather be a man. Others don't admit it, but feel that way because they wear slacks, have short hair cuts, smoke, dominate others, talk loud, work outside the home, and compete with men or try to copy them in many areas without even realizing that this is what they are doing. Subconsciously they don't want to be feminine or play the feminine role. This may go back to their poor relationship with either their father or their mother. Wives feel that a man has more advantages than a woman. Even if this were true a woman must face the fact that God made her a woman and He intended for her to be feminine so she might as well do the best job she can in being that person.

Sometimes a woman finds sex distasteful because her mother or some other relative passed on negative and unwholesome thoughts. Or perhaps as a child or teenager she had a traumatic experience involving sex play or a relationship which could turn her to hate sex. Deep therapy is then needed so she can accept the unhappy memories of the past and not have to carry them into her present marriage.

Guilt and sins of the past can be forgiven by God but they must also be forgiven by the woman herself. Sins which were done to her and not by her are not normal sins and guilt feelings should not remain. A woman can help make her husband feel like a man if she lets go of her inhibitions and enjoys sex. Sometimes it helps to go see a "sexy" movie or read a book about sex. Guilt feelings can go out the window. Whatever is enjoyable to both husband and wife should be permissible. God wouldn't have made sex feelings so strong if He didn't expect them to be fulfilled.

Many nervous symptoms such as overeating will disappear when sex is accepted as good and wholesome in a woman's life. Sometimes a wife will stay up late on purpose because she is afraid of or repulsed by sex. She sometimes eats after her husband goes to bed, because she has guilt feelings about not liking sex. She really needs the physical release of sex as much as he does and if she would enjoy it she might be able to give up her compulsive overeating and lose weight. A woman needs physical love as well as spiritual and emotional love.

Here is a recipe for love which I made up after I read what some people call a "dirty" book. It is good advice and every wife who feels unloved should copy it and leave it in her husband's top bureau drawer.

RECIPE FOR LOVE

1. Flattery and praise (even if it isn't true). Tell her she has pretty hair, nice legs, lovely skin, beautiful eyes, etc. . . . Most men don't notice what a woman is wearing, so a compliment here is helpful. Don't say, "Is that a new dress?" It might be, but it also might be an old one that you never noticed. You are safer and it is more of a compliment to say, "My dear, you look lovely in that dress," or "You look attractive tonight." *Flattery will get you everywhere.*

2. You must make her feel that she is the most important person in your life and that you would rather be with her than anyone else. She needs to be told this often.

3. Kissing should start only after the first two steps have been taken. There should be plenty of kissing and no pawing until the kisses become relaxed. Touches and light caresses should be next. Start at the top and go down.

4. When the kisses become hot, she is ready for sex.

Very few men are patient enough to use this recipe in order. That is why there are so many frigid wives.

This recipe might also help a wife to give love to an impotent husband. Of course the words and technique would be slightly different.

Here is a copy of a recent letter published in the Petaluma Argus Courier newspaper near my home town;

LETTERS TO THE EDITOR

Sex & Happy Marriage

I have been following the letters to the editors regarding the sex films shown to our young children and would like to voice my feelings. I have not had a chance to see the films, but I think that some sex education is permissable in our schools.

It has been my privilege to work the last 6 years with many overweight women and have discovered that only 2 or 3 have admitted that they enjoyed sex relations in marriage. The reasons vary, but the main reason is that parents did not give them proper sex education; most mothers and some fathers gave their daughters the thoughts that sex was dirty, disgusting, to be put up with, boring, and many other negative feelings. No wonder these little girls grew up in fear and hate of sex which is God's gift to a happy marriage. Some of your letters to the editor seem to think that sex education should wait until the teen years. I disagree. I gave a book called "The Power of Sexual Surrender" by Dr. Marie Anderson to a girl who was engaged. She was so shocked by the truth about sex relations that she did not want to get married. She waited a whole year before she could accept the fact that marriage was not all ruffles and cooking. Sex is a very vital part of marriage and when boys and girls accept it as necessary and meaningful they have a chance for a happy marriage.

Overweight persons eat for many reasons, but in my survey with most, sex is not enjoyed, but tolerated. Many women stay up and eat while their husbands go to bed because of their fear or disgust with sex which is the right of every married person. Many eat because they feel guilty because they cannot give to their husbands his desires and they are not fulfilled sexually themselves. I have statistics from past experiences with my fellow overweight club members, besides many other frustrated women who aren't overweight, that when a woman gets her thinking straight about sex, she no longer has to turn to food to satisfy her frustrated desires. I give my club members recommended books and yes, even some which are not

recommended, on the subject of sex. After some members get over their "prudish" feelings and beliefs which were handed down to them, they learn to enjoy sex so much that the weight drops off quickly. I helped two ladies save themselves from a divorce, by loaning them books and getting them to change their attitudes about sex. One has lost 32 pounds since February and is a happy wife and mother and has begun to feel a new and meaningful experience of love.

In the teen age girls group I led for two years, I learned that almost all of them came from "broken" homes or else their parents had emotional problems which disturbed the children and made them turn to food for comfort. When a child does not see love between his parents he soon feels that sex and love are wrong, and distasteful. We cannot protect our children from finding out about sex because they will get the knowledge from a source, not necessarily our own choosing. Sometimes parents wait too long to tell the innocent child about sex, and when they do, they are surprised that he already has been told by someone else. Constructive books and films do not show emotions as parents do, when sex education is given. It is very hard for parents to give sex education without showing their prejudices or feelings. This is every parent's right and privilege, but how many of us do a good job of it? At least in the schools it is given in the same way to all.

I have just finished writing a book entitled "Compulsive Overeaters' Guide," which will be published soon. In it I have two chapters entitled, "Most Fat Married People Don't Enjoy Sex," and "How Compulsive Overeaters Can Improve Their Sex Life." I have statistics to prove what I write is true. I am all for sex education in the schools and parents should be open-minded about it.

Mrs. Pearl Brians
8010 Petaluma Hill Road,
Penngrove, California
94951

IMPROVING THE OVEREATER'S SEX LIFE

Sex is a very personal subject and people hesitate to talk about it, especially overweight persons who don't enjoy it fully. One well known marriage counselor said, "Until men and women can talk about sex in groups without being embarrassed, they are HUNG-UP on sex." This was very enlightening to me. It has been my experience to get the confidence of a few overweight women who have told me why they don't enjoy sex. One main reason is because they don't feel attractive because of their fat body. They also get bored because their husbands use the same old routine and have no sense of romance with their love play. Men seem to desire sex more often than women do, perhaps because they get more satisfaction from the experience. Women need to be made aware of their sexual desires instead of trying to avoid them, or fail to admit they exist.

If husbands would play "hard to get" once in a while wives might become more interested in love play. Marriage relationships do not have to be boring, but surprisingly interesting if both persons try to make it more enjoyable. If husbands would surprise their wives with different techniques the games would bring a new zest into the home.

The Bible verse from Genesis 3;7. has caused many men and women to get the wrong attitudes about sex. It says, *"And the eyes of both of them were opened, and they knew that they were naked; and they sewed fig leaves together, and made themselves aprons."* The story of Adam and Eve is a very interesting one to read. It gives the reader the feeling that God punished woman by giving her pain in childbirth (Gen. 3;17 *"Unto the woman He said, I will greatly multiply thy conception; in sorrow thou shalt bring forth children; and thy desire shall be to thy husband, and he shall rule over thee."*) These two Bible verses alone have enough words to make the woman of today feel not only inadequate and guilty, but also even unworthy of being a person. We must help erase these false feelings if our married life is to be successful.

Since the story of Adam and Eve, women and men have had the impression that sexual intercourse must be a sin. In fact many still believe today that sexual intercourse should be used only to procreate children. This is a sad thing, because it ruins many marriages which could otherwise be happy. The attitude couples take about sex is most important for a successful marriage.

Another well-known minister-counselor and friend, Dr. Allan Hunter has given me permission to use his ideas from his booklet, "Radiant Possibilities of Marriage." He says, "Sex is certainly nothing to be ashamed of or afraid of." If accepted in gratitude, and used as a normal part of life, in its place it will prove to be a source of zest, fellowship and poise. On this basis it should help us feel at home not only with our married partner, but with ourselves and with all of life. The marriage experience should be used to create a stronger, deeper, happier and increasingly releasing bond between husband and wife. Those who value personality are learning to rejoice in the marriage-union as a glorious sacrament. They realize that on God's terms this experience can make marriage lovely. The body is not an enemy of the soul. Body, mind and soul are meant to work together in harmony. Wives no longer have to fear pregnancy because there are adequate methods of preventing conception. In place of a bad conscience and freezing anxiety, there can and should be emotional security and a sense of freedom. Birth control and birth release are meant to go together. Parenthood can be more meaningful when it is a matter of choice and the child is deliberately planned and asked for.

In some marriages a tragic misunderstanding on the part of the husband prevents the necessary teamwork. He ignorantly assumes that his wife is incapable of reaching the climax and enjoying the relationship. It never occurs to him that she has the same deep need for the release of complete sex-union that he does. Many times women themselves do not realize that they have this need. If they did, the overeating habit would become less as time improved relationships. He hurries and enjoys his own feelings and does not bother with her; to woo her or awaken her. He often misses the deep sharing experience which should satisfy both. He may even become bored with his wife, resent her lack of response, and even look for completion outside of marriage. He probably won't find it there, but he thinks he will. His wife suffers needlessly. She gets so near the climax and never arrives at a complete release and she subconsciously craves this. The deprivation can definitely harm her nervous system so much that she substitutes overeating for the real need. One of my acquaintances opened up her mind to sex as a vital part of her marriage by reading all kinds of books (both good and bad) to get a clear picture of sex as a whole. She lost 5 pounds the week she was reading what some people call "dirty" books. I don't believe there are any real dirty books; some have lessons in them, some teach us what not to do or want in love-making. No one should have to hide books or feel guilty about reading them if they want to. A "sexy" book has opened up many a wife to a happier sex life, so she doesn't have to turn to food for satisfaction.

When a wife feels deprived of real love and romance this repeated blocking of impulse may make her disgusted, not only with sex, but also with her husband, and she too may find her interest wandering. Nervous strain from such frustration has been the cause of some children becoming emotionally unfit for marriage, because disgust for it had been given to them by their mothers. No doubt she thought her negative thoughts about intercourse were a sign of purity. Actually they were symptoms of her own frustration.

Dr. Hunter says, "There are no frigid women — only clumsy men." Blaming the husband will not solve the problem. Sometimes a marriage counselor is needed for both. Good books can be of great help if both married people are willing to discuss what they read.

Many women do not experience the orgasm each time they have intercourse, and they consider themselves frigid. This is a mistake. Continued frustrations of the woman's need for the releasing climax can cause guilt, inadequacy and general unhappiness. Husbands and wives must have a deep trust and communication which will bring patience, gentleness and true interest in each other's needs. No longer do women need to reject their bodies as evil. They can be proud of their bodies and become free to develop bodily awareness. In Bonnie Prudence's book, "How To Keep Fit After Thirty", she has a chapter on "sexercises" which proves very interesting. These special exercises keep both men and women physically fit so they can fully enjoy their performance. If women could enjoy sex for sex's sake instead of looking for love with sex, they would be just as satisfied as men.

The adventure of marriage relationships comes more spontaneously to some than to others, partly because of temperament, partly because of background. Some women have had to get rid of all the old ideas planted in their minds by their prudish mothers or even fathers. Sometimes if a mother cannot talk about sex naturally to her children, it is better to give them good books to read on this subject. No emotions or prejudices are shown in most books.

Authorities on marriage insist that one of the most important preliminaries to the marriage experience is courtship, especially on the husband's part. This requires not only time and freedom from interruption, but tenderness and aroused fellow-feeling or understanding. The wife first has to be wooed and convinced that she is an important person and counts in her husband's life in other ways besides sex. The experience of sex relationship should be a mutual, shared achievement and not a selfish one. If the wife does not arrive at some satisfaction, something important is lacking. In the husband's eagerness he can easily cause her physical discomfort and mental unhappiness. Many mental disorders can be caused from shocks such as this. The husband must realize that he will be completely satisfied if he helps his wife to venture with him in joy and freedom. It takes time to achieve this ultimate goal, but it is worth working for. Haste on the part of the husband can start his wife on the road to misery and himself on the blind-alley of restlessness. The wife has the right to leisure and courtship. The husband has the responsibility to awaken her with a suitable prelude of sympathy and tenderness. The wife also has a responsibility. It is to get free as fast as she can of inhibitions and fears about sex. Her obligation is to be as relaxed and responsive as possible. She becomes aroused more slowly than her husband. If they trust each other, if they encourage each other and overlook — maybe laugh at the mistakes, they will both find the progress comes more and more enjoyable. Practice and patience are the essentials of a good marriage.

Happily married people who have reached true sexual satisfaction will take it in their stride as a sacramental health-giving part of their life together. An unhappy person who suffers from the emptiness in his own inner experience sometimes ridicules marriage relationships. The sex act in marriage is one which can be on the highest level and a stimulus toward the good and lovely — giving release of spirit, joy, vitality and poise. On God's terms it is creative as few other experiences are. When the husband and wife are able to have union of body and spirit they also create a stronger, deeper, happier bond. Because we are human and not perfect, no one *fully* expresses that love which "never fails" and which is the goal of life.

The job in marriage is to try to find out who the other person is, and then encourage him or her to act on that amazing power to fulfill the potential for growth the Creator has given him or her. We all have "masks" or phony parts of our personality which can be changed by wisdom, courage, humor and the power to care. We can help each other understand the negative moods that so often overpower us, so that each can act on his strength, not his weaknesses. The truth can be faced together and sometimes hurts, but also heals. It may be nearly impossible for husbands and wives to appreciate how each really feels, but each can try to understand. Sometimes just delaying an act caused from negative emotions can erase many problems. Be sure you don't turn to food while you are delaying an action of some other kind. Oftentimes it is because we are not physically fit, or because we are fatigued or because our spirit feels empty, that we do cruel and inconsiderate things to each other. We need to have someone who will sincerely share a faith in life with us. If someone believes in us, this may cure our secret despair. To communicate confidence is what we are to do in a marriage. Marriage should be and can be an adventure in mutual understanding, helping each partner to get emotionally free from being too dependent.

If a husband confides in his wife his innermost feelings about life, this will stimulate her to love him all the more now that she knows what he has been struggling against all by himself for so many years. This honesty on his part may also encourage her to share with him her own past feelings which make her feel inadequate. Being open with each other can be a bridge toward greater affection. Marriage is an adventure of trust, understanding and forgiveness. If there is something in the past which should be brought up and discussed, looked over, and accepted, it can be then laughed at, and buried or handed over to God. The past is gone, but it did happen so accept it as finished. Life must go on to happier heights.

WHY SO MANY FAT CHRISTIANS AND PROFESSIONAL PEOPLE?

Oftentimes I used to wonder why there were so many fat people in churches, and so many teachers, doctors, nurses and other professional people overweight. Now, after six years of study and experience working with compulsive overeaters, I realize why.

Professional people are human, and they have emotions just like we ordinary people. They have to escape from some of life's problems just like we do, and some of them turn to food. Fat people are pitied, but society usually accepts them. There are many doctors who try to help their patients lose weight, but the reason they usually don't succeed for very long periods is because they themselves are overeaters or don't understand the real problems. It is hard to expect a patient to diet when the doctor can't show a good example.

One would think that just the knowledge of health and nutrition would be enough to help teachers, doctors, psychologists, and nurses to keep physically fit. But life has proved this to be wrong. There is a great need of "understanding ourselves" as compulsive overeaters. Why we eat the wrong foods, and how our emotions affect our compulsive desires for certain starches and sweets is most important. Most professional people are under a lot of strain daily, being rushed by the fast pace of our times. They don't take time to eat proper foods, but grab a candy bar or sandwich. They eat many meals out in public where the menu is mostly refined carbohydrates. These reasons seem to be good excuses, but I believe that anyone can eat healthfully if he wishes. Even a busy professional person can have a lunch made ahead of time by someone, to take with him to the office or place of work. It can be diet jello, meat, cheese, boiled eggs, fresh vegetables, or fruit. It can be eaten in an office or car or even in the rest room if necessary. I used to work in a bakery, but I never used this excuse to grab a pastry for lunch. I was only given 10 - 15 minutes to eat and sometimes none, but as I decorated my fattening cakes I would eat my carrot sticks, celery, and protein lunch as I worked. If all overweight people would only admit that their fat comes from emotional problems and get release from anxieties, they would have more success keeping the weight off. There are thousands of people who can lose great amounts of weight yearly, but they usually gain it back at some time unless they have undergone some kind of therapy. Professional people are sometimes too proud to join a club or go to someone for emotional help. They would prefer to stay fat. Most of us hate to admit we need God or a Higher Power. We try and try to diet on our own, only to fall short of our goal. The alcoholics who get the A.A. program are very fortunate people, because they not only find sobriety but they also get a wonderful relationship with a Higher Power not known to the average person.

*   *   *

I wonder if Christians realize the reasons that they are fat. Even wonderful ministers and their wives are obese at times. It is shocking, because the average person expects these Christians to be an example of righteous living. I have talked to a few conscientious church members and ministers who have absolutely no control over their compulsive desires for too much food. What are the reasons? Many. They do not ask God to help them. They try to do it by themselves. They feel that God does not care about their weight. They have too many refreshments at social gatherings. They eat between meals. They are not sure of their emotions any more than some non-churchgoers, so they turn to food for an escape.

I feel the church is not helping the average person, who is neurotic in many ways. I've heard two well-known ministers and counselors admit that the reason they turned to the ministry is because they were so neurotic themselves that they felt the need for God in their lives. It is wonderful to know men who admit their own frailties, because then others can feel free to tell how they feel about life too.

If only the churches would get busy and have some kind of group therapy, they would have fewer fat members in their congregation. Some churches are doing this very thing. If your church is lacking in help of this kind, may I suggest a wonderful opportunity to get a group started which will be very meaningful to any members who wish to participate?

Yokefellows Inc., 209 Park Road, Burlingame, California is the headquarters for starting such a group. It is an organization that helps get groups started so lives can be filled with daily spiritual growth, which enables the members to live at peace with themselves and have fellowship and love in the group. Members are given special tests which show how they feel, and how to change any areas of their lives that need changing. Members discover that the group experience triggers the will to do what the Christian knew all along he should be doing with regard to daily prayer and fellowship with God. Most members who share their doubts, needs and failures are enabled to understand themselves better and to accept life more readily, honestly, and get the courage to "grow" spiritually. Hearing different ideas and reactions proves stimulating and helpful. Being able to "talk things out" with fellow Christians is a most rewarding experience. In order to start a group, all one has to do is write Yokefellows for information. A layman can be a leader of a group, but a minister or doctor can also lead. Sometimes professional people get the habit of monopolizing the conversation so they should read carefully the suggestions written for leading groups.

I have been in a Yokefellow group for only 6 months, but I have seen some wonderful changes take place in the members' lives. One woman member who was given up by doctors as a helpless cripple from arthritis, started to walk again after spending five years in a wheel chair. She read "Prayer Can Change Your Life", "Your Inner Child of The Past", and "The Art of Understanding Yourself". All three of these books claim that arthritis is an illness caused from deep repressed hostile feelings or resentment. I think that it is strictly a psychosomatic illness even if it is a physically painful one. After she read these books, she also studied Adele Davis' book, "Let's Get Well". In the group she let out many of her past hurts and resentments which had been buried since childhood. She began to change her thinking in such a way that she expects to be completely well soon. Others in the group have been helped with their overweight problems, smoking, sex problems, family problems, money problems, other health problems and many other symptoms. People forget that physical symptoms are really not the main problems, but they are only the body telling us that something needs to be changed in our lives or a change in attitude is needed. It is a wonderful experience to see the gradual change of people who called themselves Christians, but who were only half living.

In Dr. Osborne's book, "The Art of Understanding Yourself", he states, "There is little more love among the members of the average church than there is among Rotarians or Kiwanians. In the average church, most members do not know each other except in the most casual way. We cannot love people until we know them. The Christian church is the finest force for good we have on earth, but it is weak. Most church members feel lonely and do not feel particularly loved. The church has gradually become an institution instead of a loving fellowship." The church could strengthen its program by having several different Yokefellow groups during the week. These groups would enable the fat Christians and professional people to get the help they need in order to lose weight and keep it off.

Yokefellows Inc.,
209 Park Road,
Burlingame, California

SERENITY PRAYER

God grant me the serenity to accept the things I cannot change, the courage to change the things I can, and the wisdom to know the difference.   (*Anonymous*)

* * *

TOLERANCE

The most lovable quality any human being can possess is tolerance . . . It is the vision that enables one to see things from another's viewpoint . . . It is the generosity that concedes to others the right to their own opinions and their own peculiarities . . . It is the bigness that enables us to let people be happy in their own way instead of our way.   (*Anonymous*)

YESTERDAY, TODAY AND TOMORROW
(Anonymous)
(Read this often for help)

There are two days in each week which should cause me no worry; two days which can be free from fear and frustrations.

One of these days is YESTERDAY with its mistakes and concerns; its wrongs and oversights; its hurts and sufferings. YESTERDAY has passed, beyond my control.

All the wealth in the world can't bring back YESTERDAY: I can't change a single thing I did, I cannot take back any words I repeated. YESTERDAY is gone.

The other day I should not worry about is TOMORROW, with its possible troubles and hard work. Its hope of success or poor achievement. TOMOROW is also beyond my control.

TOMORROW will come, either with the sunshine, rain, or clouds, but it will come. Until it does, I have no choice in TO-MORROW for it is yet to come.

One day remains, and that is TODAY. I can live the experiences of just one day. It is only when I add the heavy load of YESTERDAY and TOMORROW that I will break down.

It is not the experience of TODAY that gets me so upset or frustrated — it is the painful regret of unpleasant happenings for something that occurred YESTERDAY and the dread of what might happen TOMORROW.

Let me live but one day at a time. Just for TODAY I will live.

UNITY – A CASE HISTORY

Unity has helped thousands of persons to a more constructive and happier life for many years. I became acquainted with Unity a few years ago, because several of my weight club members subscribe to their "Daily Word" monthly magazine and share its help at meetings. Unity helped a miracle take place for one special member of my club and I shall share her success story as follows;

* * *

CASE HISTORY OF JANE
Complete Recovery From Compulsive Overeating

Since my weight group members remain anonymous, I shall call her Jane. Jane called me on the telephone one day after she read an article in the paper about my Self-Improvement Club meetings.

She told me that she had just stopped smoking and had started gaining weight. She was fifteen pounds overweight, and she could not get into some of her clothes. She was unhappy with her marriage and didn't seem to enjoy life or have any outlets besides her regular housework, husband, and one little daughter. She wanted a hobby and wished for a talent to keep her busy, but was frustrated because she could not find satisfaction in living. She spent her extra time making fancy desserts and baking to keep from being bored. She liked to make chocolate fudge and chocolate cakes. These are the most fattening foods and she naturally gained weight and became a compulsive overeater since she gave up cigarettes.

Jane told me of her restlessness and how she felt no self-worth. Her husband was not able to help fill her needs. Her little girl was always being naughty, which caused Jane to be impatient and frustrated. These anxieties made her turn to food as an escape or tranquilizer. Food did not solve her problems, but she kept on eating in spite of this. She became worse each week instead of better in her compulsion for sweets and starches. She was the only member in my club who actually gained instead of losing weight.

I must admit that weight groups or clubs do not help all overeaters or all who come for help. Some are not able to grasp the type of

85

program presented and need a different kind of therapy. Jane became so compulsive that she would sometimes call me two or three times a day or night. Sometimes she would say things like this, "Oh — God — girl! You are going to kick me out of the club! I ate so much and am so unhappy! I ate a whole bag of cookies, three dishes of ice cream, three pieces of toast and jam, and so much other "junk" that I feel miserable and hate myself! What is the matter with me? I am getting worse instead of better. Why, oh why am I getting worse?"

I felt helpless, so I suggested that she needed to go to some church or minister for help. At first she didn't want to or didn't think it would help her, but as she became worse and was at "rock bottom" (as the alcoholic gets) she decided to try Unity. She went to weekly mid-meetings where the Unity program helped her gradually change into a completely different personality. She also went to the Unity Sunday services and soon I could see her whole being glow with a serene and wonderful appearance. It amazed me and others in our club. She decided to quit coming to our meetings, because she thought other members might make her become weak again. I felt that she could have shared her new found spiritual growth with them, but I had to accept her decision.

Jane lost the extra pounds and was at her normal weight again. She did this by going to Unity and getting some counseling from their leader. The biggest emotional problem Jane had was the feeling of guilt from her past. She had done something which made her feel unworthy, but Unity helped her to forgive herself, and to accept God's forgiveness thus freeing her from compulsive overeating. She gradually accepted her husband's faults, and was able to give more love to her little girl. This enabled her to have a full happy life. Unity performed a miracle in her life. Her husband used to be skeptical about religion, but now he became so interested in Jane's new personality that he decided to share it with her.

I feel a personal interest in this girl, because she was talking about getting a divorce and I helped persuade her that divorce was not the answer. If there are any unhappy people who have anxieties or needs such as Jane had, I hope they too will try Unity.

*   *   *

There are many helpful publications by Unity. Here are two which I would like to recommend for Overeaters;

"The Truth About Dieting" a booklet which tells how the Bible relates to food and overeating.

"Daily Word" a monthly daily devotional with Bible verses.

The following pages entitled BREAD OF LIFE (daily thoughts and Bible verses) are written using some ideas and quotes from Unity's Daily Word. The added thoughts about food, weight, dieting or compulsive eating are my own, put together with the positive thoughts of Unity. I am deeply grateful to Unity for their permission to quote and use these helpful ideas so I can help many overeaters who still suffer.

Address of Unity: UNITY,
LEE'S SUMMIT,
MISSOURI 64063.

BREAD OF LIFE — THOUGHTS FOR THE DAY AND BIBLE VERSES

Just because you are getting older doesn't mean you can't lose weight. Inspiration and the desire to give up compulsive eating can come to young and old alike. It can come and flow through all who seek it. Sometimes we hold onto these old eating patterns even though we want to release them and get rid of them. Can it be partly because we don't know how to use the time we used to spend in eating? Have we found a substitute for food? Faith in God and the power He can give us will make us unafraid to give up all these bad eating habits. We can outgrow our compulsions for too many sweets and starches. We can begin to think clearly. Right now, this minute we can feel God's presence in our lives. Let us have the courage to release old ideas about eating and open our mind to a new fresh inspiration from God.

"But it is the spirit in a man, the breath of the Almighty, that makes him understand." Job 32;8

*   *   *

God does not choose certain persons or certain conditions for healing. He can heal all compulsive eaters no matter who they are. There are none "too far gone" or "too fat" for healing. *"With God all things are possible".* Let us remember this when we ask Him to take away our compulsion. Let's not be afraid or disturbed because at first it seems hard to let go. Let us hold fast to the belief that release from food can come. We do not have to beg Him to heal our thoughts. He is life and health and His presence is always in us. What we need to do is to open our minds and get a clearer picture of God and His truth which is in each one of us. Let us believe wholeheartedly that someday we can "be well" from compulsive eating. *"With God all things are possible."* Matt. 19;26

*   *   *

The Spirit of God within me, which first made me a person, then helped me to grow, is always looking out for my welfare. I can turn my attention to this great spiritual power within me and all my eating problems will be under control. The spirit of God within me is the source of my strength to keep from snacking between meals. Its renewing power moves in and makes me well in all ways. The spirit of God within me blesses my body so that I can use it productively instead of destroying it with too much food. I will have freedom from anxiety about overeating because the Spirit in me gives me a sense of security. I am free from over concern about what others do because I realize that they too have an indwelling Spirit to help their needs. *"Cast your burden on the Lord."* Psalms 55;22

*   *   *

I refuse to let outside pressures disturb me so much that I will overeat. I refuse to let myself feel pushed so I will eat. I no longer tell myself that just because I'm crowded for time doesn't mean I have to grab some fattening food. I will let go of the stress and strain of every day living and take each thing as it comes. I will move and act in peace and harmony because God is with me. I have strength to do all I need to do because God will give it to me. My disposition will be happier and I won't have to overeat. I'll take things one at a time. "First things first." I'll concentrate on the thing at hand and have faith in its results. I can be confident that God will help manage my affairs. *"In quietness and in confidence, shall be your strength."* Isa. 30;15

*   *   *

Psychologists tell us that we must approve of ourselves before we can maintain emotional or mental health. I can look at myself today and see myself as God sees me. I see myself as a whole person. I don't have to let the judgement of others tear me down and make me feel unworthy. I don't have to let food become an obsession just because someone's words or actions have offended me. God's healing power can give me peace. My feelings become in harmony with God's. I am aware of His goodness to me so I don't need extra foods. As I let go of self-condemning thoughts I can eat sensibly and it will be easier to approve of myself. I'll get a new thin image of myself and believe that I am loved by God.

"Happy is he who has no reason to judge himself for what he approves." Rom. 14;22

*   *   *

We may think we could stop overeating if we had more money, a new house, a certain job, a different family, but what we really want is an opportunity to express our creative selves. When we let God bless all our affairs, we discover that He will provide all that is needed. He will give us opportunities to use our energy into constructive ways which will be opened to us. Whatever is needed to make our lives happy and satisfying will come.

"Prove me herewith . . . if it will not open you the windows of heaven, and pour you out a blessing, that there shall not be room enough to receive it." Mal. 3;10

*   *   *

God's will for me is designed for the practical, down to earth person that I am in this world. I am in this world for a definite reason. I can apply God's spirit in my daily life. He can show me the practical purpose for my life so I won't be frustrated and turn to food for comfort. God will reveal greater good each day as I live my life. The inner knowledge can be used by me to control my eating, my relationships with others, and each activity of the day. I am a real expression of God as I keep my feet firmly on His path. The moments of communion with Him can be transmitted into creative energy instead of compulsive eating.

"If you know these things, blessed are you if you do them." John 13;17

*   *   *

An affirmation is a statement of truth about any person or condition. If you know it is true that you are compulsive and cannot eat small amounts of refined carbohydrates, then for you is to give them up entirely. Wishful thinking to be a normal eater when you aren't ready is no use. To know the truth about your condition is the first step to self change. This facing the facts about your compulsion can be used as a tool to improve it, especially when you admit it to God. It has been said that God has no hands but our own. The word of God comes from our mouths. We can let our words speak goodness and good things will be established in our lives. The words we speak and the way we act are what help us to accomplish our daily growth.

"Let the words of my mouth and the meditation of my heart be acceptable in Thy sight." Psalms 19;14

*   *   *

Life is always enjoyable when we stay on a proper healthful eating plan. We like ourselves and can be congenial with others. If we do all we can to establish a peaceful home and atmosphere we won't feel the need to overeat. This not only helps us, but inspires others to do the same. When we do our part of being a constructive person we meet cooperation with others. All persons want to live in harmony with each other and enjoy life, and most people are ready to make an effort if they get even slight encouragement. Let us determine that no matter who tries to bother us, we are going to live in peace and harmony. We are going to enjoy life, and we are going to make life more enjoyable for others, without eating fattening foods.

"Be at peace with one another." Mark 9;50

*   *   *

How can I enjoy my life? By staying on three moderate meals a day? What can I do to better myself and others? By losing weight? As I approach life in this attitude of self-discipline, I find that there are always ways in which I can improve. Not in the physical ways only, but the spiritual, and emotional life can be improved. I may see ways to improve my disposition. I can consider regular exercise. I may decide to give up some unimportant activities for those more important activities. I may need to stop procrastinating. If there are any other areas of my life with which I feel dissatisfied or restless, or feel failing in any way, I pray for guidance and knowledge, so that I may take certain actions and steps to improve myself. I will find joy in every day as I make the effort to improve and grow.

"We are to grow up in every way." Eph. 4;15

*   *   *

Yesterday we may have accepted a belief in our weakness to overeat. We may have thought we had no control. We may have felt limited, imperfect and faulty in doing differently. But today we are not going to give in to our compulsive eating. We are going to release it to God. We will deny our hunger pangs the satisfaction of overeating. First, we can give up all negative thoughts and actions. Then we can really know that God will give us strength and good health. Each time we give up certain tempting foods, let us replace these desires with new ideas and concepts. My mind and body are unlimited and I am a perfect creation of God.

"Behold, I will bring to it health and healing, and I will heal them." Jer. 33;6

* * *

As we change our wrong eating habits to better ones we will rise above the thought that we can't lose weight. We know that over-weight is not part of God's plan for us. As we think of ourself as eternal being, we hold steady faith and in our conviction to eat properly. What are the opportunities we can take toward our goal? Have we taken chances of eating the wrong foods? Has our desire to lose weight failed? How can we stand firm in our belief? Has some-one treated us unfairly? In God's plan for us and our life, there is always love and justice, and in God we are always secure. Thank you God, for your loving presence ever in me. Your power at work in my life is with me.

"We know that in everything God works; for good with those who love Him." Rom. 8;28

* * *

I cannot give without receiving and I cannot receive without giving. When I give of my time to exercise and diet and live right I receive a healthy body and sound mind. When I receive this healthy body and sound mind I will share this knowledge in order to help others. Nothing is worth keeping unless it is also worth sharing. I thank God, for the Spirit within me which helps me to retain this new mind and body. Thank You for the vitality and strength I re-ceive from eating and living with Your will. Let me be a blessing to others. Let my happiness bring a gift of joy to others. Let me share my prosperity with others. May I feel a joy in giving and receiving.

"Every good gift and every perfect gift is from above." James 1:17

* * *

When we have a problem such as: "What shall I do? How shall I meet this change? What road shall I take? Which way of life shall I choose?", we can go to a counselor, a minister, a friend or relative. This is good and we are fortunate if this person to whom we turn for help has the Spirit of God in him so he can help us feel that Spirit. Our final decision to lose weight, exercise, read good books, pray and live right are still our own choice and it is up to us to get started on the pathway which we feel God wants us to follow. We are not alone in this new health venture. Thousands have a weight problem. Thousands of people are compulsive overeaters. Think of many who struggle along the way of life. It is not easy, but the Spirit in us gives us the power to take the steps we know we must take to lose weight. We can and will do it unhesitatingly and with courageous hearts.

"Lead me in Thy path and teach me. For Thou art the God of my Salvation; for Thee I wait all day long." Psalms 25;5

*   *   *

We do not have to keep overeating each day, being unhappy, unforgiving, resentful and upset. We cannot forget, but we can forgive and we must if we want to lose weight and stop eating compulsively. An overeater cannot afford resentments. We must make a conscious effort to forgive and perhaps forget if we can. We need to take time to bless the persons or situations that have been a source of our unhappiness. It is very important for our serenity, our happiness, health and well being to let go of any bitterness, any hurt, any resentment or disappointment. We need to release them and let them go. As we feel God's spirit in us we can let them go.

"Forgive our debts, as we forgive our debtors." Matt. 6:12

*   *   *

It's never too late to lose weight or to change my thinking about food. What are the things I would like to see changed in my life besides my weight? Would I like to enjoy better health? Would I like to have more security and more money? Would I like to be more appreciated and loved? Would I like to have better working conditions? It doesn't matter what I would like to see changed in my life, change can come as I change my thinking. This is a step-by-step process, one step at a time. A thought-by-thought process. Before we take a step we must believe it to be the right step. I must constantly be aware of negative thoughts and change them to positive ones. Ill health and overweight thoughts can be changed to good health and trimness. It can be done. I will begin now and shall succeed for God is with me.

"For as he (man) thinketh in his heart, so is he." Prov. 23;7

*   *   *

No matter how much I am overweight, my dreams, goals, and high hopes are attainable, for God fulfills every desire of my heart. I must have a strong desire to lose weight if I expect Him to fill my needs to obtain a weight loss. In me is a power to be slim, healthy, strong, and vitally alive. In me is the ability to be successful, to be prosperous, and to achieve the best and fullest life. In me is a source of happiness and joy. In me is power that comes from God, power that is my divine inheritance. I am one with God and with His help, I can lose weight and keep it off. The joy of normal living can be mine as I know that God is inspiring me, I know it; I claim it; I accept it.

"Take delight in the Lord and He will give you the desires of your heart." Psalms 37;4

* * *

When we are praying for a trimmer body or a healthier one, let us get rid of all thoughts of anxiety and know that God, the Healer is with us. When others are ill let us do the same. Let us look past appearances and keep our faith centered in God. He can heal our lives and the lives of others for whom we pray. His power is ceaseless and perfect. Let us believe He can help us as we pray for healing. Praying and not believing gets us nowhere. Let us picture our bodies trim and healthy; always keep that picture so the Spirit of healing can take over. It is taking over now as we pray.

"I will restore health to you, and your wounds I will heal." Jer. 30;17

* * *

We need to bless the past and learn from it. We need to release it and let it go. As we feel God's spirit in us we can let it go.

"Forgive our debts, as we forgive our debtors." Matt. 6;12

* * *

Sometimes I find myself wanting to tell others what to do. But I realize I have no right, so I place them in God's hands, because I know each has his own Spirit to guide him. When I find myself being responsible for others who aren't losing weight, I put them in God's care because I cannot afford to be over concerned. I might "eat about it" myself. God, let me do what I can to help my loved ones and others to lose weight; but I should not try to do for them the things they need to do for themselves. I can only be an example. Let me be thoughtful and willing to let go of their lives so that God's presence can fill them.

"Great is your faith; be it done for you as you desire." Matt. 15;28

How we handle money that comes to us has a great deal to do with our prosperity. Let us sit down and decide what luxury foods that are fattening we can quit buying. We must keep balance and order in all our affairs. Let us spend each dollar for worthwhile goods than can enrich our lives. Let's express God's positive power in our financial activities. It is only good judgement to buy healthful foods which won't make us gain weight. Even the normal eaters in our families don't need some of the refined carbohydrates we used to buy. Let us use our money wisely for everything.

"Moreover it is required of stewards that they be found trustworthy." 1 Cor. 4;2

*   *   *

Freedom is a feeling we have when we are able to make a decision, when a decision should be made. We can be free to decide to give up all our "binge" foods until we reach our desired weight goal. This one decision can free us from all the compulsive overeating we used to do. We are free to take action which will lead us to a happier, healthier life. Every time of decision is a time of opportunity to decide on the way we will eat and live. Our thoughts and attitudes will carry us to the proper actions so we can develop our talents, and bodies. We can take a stand for things we know are right and good. We can let go of some things which have limited us for proper action. Let us take each day's decisions one at a time and be free to follow God's will in them. As we pray for guidance, we shall see our way clearly; and we will have a sense of freedom.

"If the Son makes you free, you will be free indeed." John 8; 36

*   *   *

No matter what stands between your way of losing weight and the kind of life you want to have, you can and are free to change it. You are free to let go of all negative or limited thoughts for staying fat. You are free to rise up and be free of depression or unhappy emotions. You are free to change your diet to one of high protein and other health-giving foods which will help you lose weight. You can change your pattern of life into constructive and positive actions. You can claim this freedom instantly, by trusting in God to guide, inspire and give you courage to do all these things you desire. You have the power and ability to do and to be all that you long to do and be. Through the God spirit in you, your powers and abilities will be endless and you can feel and think harmonious living.

"For freedom Christ has set us free." Gal. 5;1

Perhaps the most important quality that should be expressed toward life is the love of God, in which there is no upset, no disturbance whatever. It is only the inner irritations we have toward life that keeps us from a real sense of happiness and peace of mind. When we allow ourselves to overeat and become upset everything seems to go wrong. We find ourselves doing things or saying things that are misunderstood. But when we are aware of the love of God at work in us, we can make a sincere effort to pour forth this love to all persons enabling us to stay on a proper eating plan.

"He who is slow to anger has great understanding." Prov. 14;29

* * *

Many of us overeaters think we are rushed for time, so we grab a sandwich or cookie or candy bar instead of sitting down to a healthful meal. There is time enough for all things that are important to us. We need more wisdom in the use of the time we have. We need to plan it with good judgment in the way we handle the things we need to do. At the beginning of the day, if we meditate and make our plans according to how we feel God wants us to live, we will have no trouble. There is time enough and strength enough for every task, every hour, and God constantly replenishes our strength within. We have the ability to accomplish successfully and well whatever is before us. We can let God work through us so we won't have to grab a bite, but take time for three nutritious meals a day.

"This is the day which the Lord has made." Psalms 118;24

* * *

Peace and harmony result when people pray and work together in a spirit of cooperation. Often inharmonious attitudes and actions are changed for the better when just one person consciously gives sincere and loving help. We won't have to overeat if we meet inharmonious situations in prayer, and direct them into constructive and helpful actions.

"Do not neglect to show hospitality to strangers for thereby some have entertained angels unawares." Heb. 13;2

* * *

Little children have open minds. They do not reject new ideas, but are eager to know more, to learn and soak up knowledge. We too must become more childlike and open-minded about our new health plan, which is necessary for losing weight. We should not reject any ideas in this book until at least we have tried them. There is an old saying, "Don't knock it until you have tried it." We can learn by trying the ideas and keep what is helpful to ourselves. We can let our minds be free to experience new ideas and actions. We can be inspired by these new ideas and have a new enthusiasm for living.

"Except ye turn, and become as little children, ye shall in no wise enter into the kingdom of heaven." Matt. 18;3

*   *   *

What a great joy it is to be able to meet a crisis with poise. We don't have the craving to "eat about it," and it gives us pleasure to realize that we are reacting with love and patience where we used to shout with anger. It is rewarding to know that we are in control of our eating and can stand firm when someone needs our strength. As we let God's spirit dwell in us, it takes charge with poise under all circumstances. We rely on this Spirit to see us through, and lift us up, and give us strength. We must pray and let God take charge of our emotional nature. We can use this strength to change our eating plan, to grow more healthful, so we can become more peaceful and calm.

"And the peace of God, which passes all understanding, will keep your hearts and your minds in Christ Jesus." Phil. 4;7

*   *   *

When we work with the attitude that we are working for God, we know we cannot be unjustly treated; we know that our abilities cannot be overlooked; we know that our efforts and work will turn out as they should. We can increase our blessings by trying to be more pleasant and by changing our attitude toward work.

"And every good work that he undertook in the service of the house of God ... he did with all his heart, and prospered." 2nd Chron. 31;21

*   *   *

Joy and enthusiasm are catching. When we stay on a good eating plan and are enthusiastic about our new way of life, we meet with others who will also have good feelings about following our example. If you get up each morning happy and ready for the day you will be rewarded by joy and success. Sometimes you might get up reluctantly, but at least try to work on this plan of enthusiasm. It might awaken a better feeling within you so you will be capable of doing more than you previously expected. Be thankful for those you know who have the good spirit of love in them.

"Break forth into joy, sing together." Isa. 52;9

We who use this book's meditations and thoughts find that our life and weight problem become easier to manage. We know that the habit of prayer and good thought prepares our way for discipline that brings happiness and satisfaction. To start the day thus, assures us that all that comes or concerns us will be brought into order. We find that there is a smoothness in our lives that flows along enabling us to accomplish things happily.

"Keep steady my steps according to thy promise, and let no iniquity get dominion over me." Psalms 119;113

* * *

There are many changing conditions around us that may disturb or upset us. We sometimes feel no peace. But the world is not the place to look for peace. Peace comes from within ourselves. If we rely on the power of God within us, we are able to meet life with confidence. When we are troubled about some situation in our lives, we must hold fast to our faith and refuse to be dismayed by appearances. We must believe in the good and it will come.

"Be of good cheer, I have overcome the world." John 16;33

* * *

Every time I want to eat the wrong foods, I will say, "Relax, and let go. God is in charge." I can be thankful that His powers are in me, and He gives me the wisdom to make the right decisions to meet every situation. I will not allow any anxieties or worries to make me eat. In spite of them I can stay on my diet and not falter. I trust God's spirit to strengthen me, and fill me with a newness of release and power over temptation.

"According to the riches of his glory he may grant you to be strengthened with might through his spirit in the inner man." Eph. 3;16

* * *

I will not put off losing weight another day. This is the time. The time to meet this need is now. I don't have to wait 'till Monday or some other time. I need to get rid of excess pounds and I have made up my mind that now is a good time to begin. This will be an important part of my prayers and daily thinking. I am in need of a good diet, so I will eat right. God can help me to understand which paths to take in order to reach my desired goal. I must have peace and harmony in my life and one way to get it, is to *stop overeating*. With God's help I shall do just that.

"Now is the acceptable time." 2nd Cor. 6;2

We must be patient with ourselves if we go off our diet. Condemning and hating ourselves only makes things worse. We must have patience with ourselves as well as with others. We should not condemn ourselves if we do not measure up to what we hoped to attain. Patience with our family, friends and others requires this kind of spirit.

"Let Patience have her perfect work." James 1;4

*   *   *

A perfect body is God's will for me. Realizing this, I will do all I can to regulate and renew all parts so that my body can function properly. I will give myself a proper diet, exercise and rest. I will thank God for my health and be willing to do my part in keeping healthy. I will have a free feeling of wholeness.

"Do you know that you are God's temple, and that God's spirit dwells in you?" I Corin. 3;16

*   *   *

Thought control is the basis for the control over our eating and all our daily actions. In fact we act and react to life according to the dominant trends of thought active in our mind. Yet when we try to control our eating and thinking through the use of will power, we find that it is an almost impossible task. When we allow God to work through us we can become filled with new ideas and changes come easier. As we surrender our thinking to something greater than ourselves, we will get satisfactory results. We can let God's intelligence guide our eating and daily lives.

"You will know the truth and the truth will make you free." John 8;32

*   *   *

This book's ideas should not be read just once — *it should be studied daily.* It will be a benefit to your life if you take time to sit still and commune with its contents. It must become a part of your thoughts and feelings and your consciousness. When you are truly relaxed and in tune with God's spirit, this book will give you power to do all you need to do to live more healthfully and to lose weight. You will let go of all thoughts and desires for sweets and starches and let your mind dwell on the real needs of your body and mind. Close your eyes and say, "I am relaxed. I don't need any special foods. I am content to live an orderly life." Then think of how these thoughts will stay with you all during the day.

"I can do all things through Him who strengthens me." Phil. 4;13

Some of us overeaters have felt unjustly treated by others. We've eaten excess foods because we didn't know how to handle our hostility. We didn't think of turning to God instead of eating. If we do pray about being unjustly treated, we will find that things seem to straighten themselves out. Perhaps this is because we are straightened out in our thinking. As we pray, we realize that nothing can be taken from us that is our own. As we hold on to our faith in the good, we discover that it is our own. As we hold on to our faith in the good we discover that our good is established in God. Other persons' good is also established in God and their blessings come as they were meant to come. God, who is love is ever at hand to establish a perfect balance.

"But the path of the just is the shining light, that shineth more and more unto the perfect day." Prov. 4;18

* * *

There is no condition that cannot be healed, for there are present within every person mighty healing forces. We all want to be whole and perfect in every way. Even when we appear to be ill, everything works in us for life and healing. We should *never feel* that any condition is hopeless, we should *never say* some condition is hopeless. Healing is always God's will and it is always possible. Let us pray for healing and believe in it.

"With God, all things are possible." Matt. 19;26

* * *

We will not have any difficulty learning which are the right foods to eat if we keep openminded and think what is best for our health. We must not set up any mental blocks by thinking we can't change our desires for certain foods. Our thoughts for today can be strong and powerful and we must hold on to the new will we have acquired, so that we will be free from negative thinking, and release the powers and potentials within us. We can do all things with God's help. We are capable of success and we are meant for success.

"Let the mind be in you, which was also in Christ Jesus." Phil. 2;3

* * *

How freeing it is to realize that it is never too late to diet, to change, to improve, and I can always begin again. All that has gone before can be a blessing to me, if I think of it as part of my growth. Even the experiences that may now seem regrettable take their place in the overall pattern of things when I look at my life as coming out of the darkness into the light. I am never at the end of anything but always at a place of beginning. I take one step at a time toward my goal, which sometimes seems far away, but each step leads me closer. I must not step back, but go ahead with confidence. Let any unhappy thoughts or feelings about others be replaced with positive ones; happy, loving and forgiving ones. It is not too late and I can begin again.

"Forgetting what lies behind . . . I press on toward the goal." Phil. 3;13

*   *   *

Wisdom is the ability to know what is right to do at any given moment of the day. God's spirit in us can keep us on the right food plan and it can give us understanding of our health and body needs. The spirit and mind can give us insight and awareness of each day's actions. If you ever lack wisdom say, "God, what do You want me to do? What do You want me to say?" We must make the decisions which will bring satisfactory results. This will be a source of light and guidance. If we ask God for help, He will show the way to our highest capacity. Everything will be kept in order if we ask to be shown the way.

"Those who are wise shall shine like the brightness of the firmament; and those who turn many to righteousness; like the stars for ever and ever." Dan. 12;2

*   *   *

Freedom is a feeling we have when we make a decision to entirely give up refined carbohydrates. Now we don't have to worry about gaining weight, we don't have to worry about being tempted, because these foods are out of our food plan, at least until we reach our goal. Man was created free — not of responsibilities and obligations — but free to take charge of his thoughts, words, and actions, so that he is not driven but led, by God's spirit within. Every time of decision is a time of opportunity — opportunity to decide on the way we will go, on the thoughts and attitudes we will keep, on the course of activity that will best develop our talents and abilities. Sometimes our decision is to take a stand for goodness. Sometimes our decision is to let go of something bothering us. Every day offers us many decisions. We are free to follow the mind of God in us and as we pray for a clear way we will have a sense of freedom.

"If the Son makes you free, you will be free indeed." John 8;36

*   *   *

Christmas time; At this season of the year — we may be pressured to hurry, to buy, to get things done. If we allow ourselves these pressures, we can make this Christmas full of tenseness, anxiety and even irritability. This is not how Jesus would want us to celebrate His birth. This should be a time of joy and peace. All the things we buy or do to make Christmas special, are not as important as the spirit of Christmas. If we hold to this spirit, we can not be caught up in the anxiety of others about us, but feel the real joy of the season. We can do what we need to do without strain. We can enjoy the days before Christmas and after Christmas as well as celebrating that special day which marks the birth of Jesus, man of peace.

"His name will be called . . . Prince of Peace." Isa. 9;6

* * *

Happiness is a living awareness of God. All your affairs can be placed in His care. Release them and know that the best answers will be on their way. To enjoy being a happy person is to be free of anxiety. Happiness leads to health. Negative thoughts about overeating hinder our bodily functions. Good health comes to every truly happy person. Thoughts of joy free you of unhappy situations and are an inspiration to others. Your greatest expectation will come if you enjoy growth and knowledge.

"A cheerful heart is good medicine." Prov. 17;22

* * *

My thoughts and feelings about food, diet and health are with me constantly. I must be sure that my heart and mind have only the best motives that will produce the best for me. Do I want a day free from compulsive eating? Can I prepare myself with the right foods so that there will be no excuses to go off my diet? *Am I thinking of my health more than my desires of taste?* Am I receptive to the ideas which will keep me strong? I will start my day each morning with a quiet time to feel God's presence in me for the day's happenings. He starts me on my good day, refreshed, and ready for all that comes. I will have positive reactions to everything that enters my life.

"The word is a lamp to my feet and a light to my path." Psalms 119;105

* * *

The few minutes a day that I read this book will affirm the truth for my life and others. It can set the tone of my day. It can give me power to take the day and show love to myself and others. I can think about myself, my life, and affairs that are before me today, and I can have faith and the assurance of eating and living right. I feel renewed inwardly and relaxed in my mind and body. Old thoughts, worries, anxieties, and pressures drop from me. I let go and let God; I know that all is well.

"Be still and know that I am God." Psalms 40;10

*   *   *

In the morning when you wake, before you turn yourself in bed, think "Forgive, forget, call down, upon each head." If you can't do this, then don't get out of bed. Unity sent this pamphlet out. A man said, "I've been in bed two weeks; when can I get up?" Some of us would never get up if we had to give up past resentments first. We don't realize how the past can make us overeat in the present, but it does. It is very important to get rid of old hurts and bad feelings. Being thankful that the past is gone is one way to release unhappiness or wrong thoughts of the past. Many times we are so busy trying to work out our life's problems and are so concerned about what others do or say that we forget the blessings we have. We forget to say, "Thank you" to God, and to people as well. To express thanks sets up a greater appreciation for life in us, so that we continually find new cause for rejoicing.

"Forget not all His benefits." Psalms 103;2

*   *   *

It is not always easy to get along with people. But it is good to try! Some of us find it difficult to get along with ourselves! Especially when we overeat. We may not like our own thoughts and actions. If we try to understand ourselves, we can better accept ourselves. We can begin to change and improve many things. The more we understand ourselves, the less we will think about food. Our getting along with people is mostly understanding them. Prayer is a way to understanding. It gives us patience, and enables us to be tolerant. It keeps us from speaking words we may regret or it keeps us from doing the things best left undone. When we understand others our relationships with them improve.

"Making your ear attentive to wisdom and inclining your heart to understanding." Prov. 2;2

*   *   *

The conversations we have with others are often a source of enlightenment to us, but the conversations we have with ourselves affect us more than we realize. If someone tells us to stay on a high protein diet, but we tell ourselves we don't want to — who has more influence on us — the other person or ourselves? Do we build ourselves up or do we run ourselves down? De we ever say to ourselves, "I'll never get this weight off!", or do we say, "I'm going to get this weight off!". Do we say to ourselves, "I don't deserve success and a trim body," or do we say, "I deserve and will get a trim body, so I will find happiness, joy and goodness for myself." Take this idea, you have a spirit of love, courage, and faith which will help you to understand your true needs. Through God's love and spirit in you, serenity and confidence will come if you keep telling yourself the positive things. Knock out those old negative thoughts — remember they are in the past. Venture forth to a brighter future.

"Thou dost keep Him in Perfect Peace." Isa. 26;3

*   *   *

Reading parts of this book can help us to become better persons each day. We must believe that we are changing and then we will become changed. We can bring out the good in ourselves and others by releasing any feelings of uneasiness. We should remind ourselves constantly that we are better than we appear to be. God's spirit is in each one of us, and we can call on this goodness at any time.

"Do not judge by appearance, but judge with right judgment." John 7;24

*   *   *

If you ever wake up feeling "So what!", about life, feeling not needed, not important to anyone, the first thing you should remember is that even though you feel that way, it is not true. You are needed and you are important. Every person is important. We are loved by God. We have His Spirit in us and we can help someone else who might be feeling unimportant. Look around you, find someone you can help. You have the capacity to help someone because God has given you this gift. You can pray for others and have faith in them, and give them love.

"See what love the Father has given us." 1 John 3;1

*   *   *

Most of the time our greatest need for forgiveness is forgiveness of ourselves. For when we feel bitter and unforgiving toward some person or about some situation, we need a blessing more than the person or the situation that seems to be the cause. We do not have to remain in a bitter or unforgiving state of mind or heart. We can rise out of personal feelings or personal hurts. We can say to ourselves, "I am filled with the forgiving love of God, and if He forgives, then I can also forgive all people, myself included."

"The Son of man has authority on earth to forgive sins." Matt. 9;16

* * *

Some of us get upset when the weather is too hot, or too cold, or too foggy, or too rainy. These are all parts of nature and in this life we must learn to accept the weather as it comes. We won't have so much need to overeat when we learn to accept things we cannot change. Our emotions make us turn to food for comfort or escape. Dissatisfaction about the weather is not necessary or good. It only hurts our thinking. All kinds of weather is necessary for the Divine Order of things. The weather brings growth and expansion and production. We must seek the same Divine Order in our own lives. A variety of experiences helps us become more mature. Where there is a need for adjustment, let us pray for the guidance to change our affairs. When there is a need for harmony, peace, and happiness, let us pray for a Divine Order in our relationships with others. Let us ask that this good order start in ourselves first. We can stop over-eating, which will be a true beginning of Divine Order.

"You will seek me and find me when you seek me with all your heart." Jer. 29;13

* * *

A good diet leads me to love more.
A good diet lets me be open-minded.
A good diet leads me to joy and slimness.
A good diet keeps me strong, physically and emotionally.
A good diet leads me to good thoughts.
A good diet keeps me at peace with myself.
A good diet helps me accept others.
A good diet takes away my fears of being tempted by fattening foods.
A good diet unites me with a new spiritual life.

"Follow me." Matt. 16;24

* * *

If I feel I need to lose weight and can't, then I can pray for the right direction to guide me, so I will not be so dissatisfied with myself. I pray to be shown areas of my life that need changing and improving. I pray for the strength to give up my "binge" foods, so I can seek the things in life which are more meaningful. I'll get a new picture of myself as happy and trim. I'll open my mind to health books and proper diet plans. I'll see myself growing spiritually instead of physically fat. My mind, body and soul and every need can be improved with God's help.

"For he satisfieth the longing soul, and filleth the hungry soul with goodness." Psalms 107;9

*   *   *

When the challenge to lose weight presents itself to us, we may be fearful because the new way of eating is different. This is understandable. But remembering that God is with us enables us to meet this new change and meet it well and willingly. We can help ourselves even more if we find someone else who is also trying to lose weight. We can give ourselves and that person help, just by discussing our weight problem. We can get and receive encouragement because we will realize we are not alone in our dilemma. There are thousands of unhappy overweight people who are also compulsive on sweets and starches just as we are. We are not odd balls. There are hundreds of other sneak eaters who hide food or only eat in private. All these persons are seeking some kind of security, but turn to food because they have not found it. You can share this book with others who will listen.

"They shall be safe." Ezek 34.27

*   *   *

We want things in our life to work out harmoniously and we want to lose weight. We want to go along each day without friction or fuss. We want a Divine Order in our lives. The new disciplined eating plan can become so powerful in our daily lives that it is our first reaction. To eat right — live right — think right — and be the right kind of person we want to be. We are making gradual changes to improve daily. We are learning new thoughts about accepting ourselves and others. All things good fall into place according to the best plans and schedules if we ask God to guide us. When we admit our need for His help and humble ourselves, God becomes active in all our affairs.

"Commit your way to the Lord; trust in him, and he will act." Psalms 37;5

*   *   *

Most of us want peace more than anything else in the world. We yearn for peace of mind, peace of heart, peace in our home, on our jobs, with our friends, and in the world. Peace is necessary to our well-being. We work more efficiently when we are at peace with ourselves, and our craving to overeat is not so strong. When we feel real peace we actually forget about food. Our mind and bodies function more effectively if there is no mental or emotional turmoil. Peace can be ours now, today — not tomorrow or next year. We find peace when we stop thinking that other persons can hurt us or interfere with our lives; when we stop trying to force our way on others, when we start expecting only good to come to us, when we express love in all our human relations, when we open our minds and hearts to God's direction. I am at peace, and I don't have to use food to calm my nerves, I trust God to regulate and perfect my life and affairs. I trust God to bring forth good in every experience.

"Great peace have those who love thy law." Psalms 119;165

* * *

God is my strength and courage. I will stay on my diet with Him to guide me. His strength within me makes me equal to keeping fit and willing to consume the proper foods. Through His power I will have the physical strength, the mental stability, and the emotional serenity I need in order to continue on my new way of life. I will increase my strength by saying to myself; "I am strong and God is with me. I feel strength and courage within myself to be able to lose weight and realize that anything is possible with God's help. His life is my life; His power is my power; His strength is my strength. Knowing that God is helping me keep strong keeps me steady and unmoved and fearless when fattening foods are set before me."

"The Lord is the stronghold of my life; of whom shall I be afraid?" Psalms 27;1

* * *

When it seems that I have nothing to be joyful about, when I am tempted to overeat and give way to self-pity or depression, I am brought out of these feelings by opening myself to the idea of joy. I may not feel joyful; but there is that in me which is my source of joy, which is my strength, which sustains me. The joy of God is like a wellspring within me. It can never be depleted; it is always there, waiting to well up in me, to fill my heart, to overflow into my life. I change the attitude of my thoughts and feelings through taking words of goodness and holding on to them. I can be uplifted just by thinking about these words; I meditate upon them; I speak them silently and aloud. I do not have to try to force joy; I do not have to pretend to be joyful. In my spirit I am joyful. The joy of God is within me; it uplifts and blesses me.

"That my joy may be in you, and that your joy may be full." John 15;11

* * *

Each word of prayer we speak — spoken aloud or simply taken into our thought — brings a certain reaction. Words are not empty. They carry power. Also our thoughts carry power. They can be positive or negative, whichever we choose them to be. Let us make our thoughts and words carry out good works. Let us think good about ourselves so we will feel worthy of losing weight. We are worthy to have a healthy body, a happy life, and good experiences every day. We need to be enlightened mentally, physically, and spiritually. Even as we speak and pray our vision expands, and our faith is quickened and we see the light of how to change and we hold on to the goodness about ourselves and continue in our search for a complete sense of wholeness. We know the way we are to go. Nothing will change us from this newness.

"So then faith cometh by hearing, and hearing by the word of God." Rom. 10;17

* * *

Whatever we experience today, let us remember that God is with us. We may have challenging happenings, but to be challenged is to grow. We may have experiences that bring about change in us — in our thoughts, our feelings, our actions — but it can be a change for the better, a change that means growth. All of life is growth, and who would choose to stop growing! Whatever we meet today, let us name it good. Let us look for the good in every condition, every situation. When we look for the good, good is revealed. Certainly, to worry, to fret, to grieve is not the way to handle that which challenges us. Certainly to eat and gain weight is not the way to handle that which we can't accept or change. We discover sometimes that the experiences which seemed to demand the most of us brought us the greatest blessing.

"God is with you in all that you do." Gen. 21;22

* * *

Healing can come quickly, even when a person is very ill. The body is most responsive to prayer, to ideas of life and strength and health. We can also lose weight quickly if we pray about it and trust in God to help us. When we pray for healing for ourselves or for another, let us pray in the faith that God's will is life and wholeness, that every tendency of mind and body is toward healing. Let us not feel depressed or sad because of an apparent condition. Rather, let us keep our faith in God, so He can heal us and help us to lose weight. His power can work through us. Let us thank Him that we have the knowledge to eat the right things and the courage to stick to a diet long enough to get results. It is wonderful to realize that we no longer have to remain fat, or sick or unhappy. It is God's will for us to be well and slim and He is working through many channels and in many ways to promote healing. This book was written by someone who felt the blessings from God in her life enough to be able to put them down in words. God will work through you so you can get all your heart's desires.

"Then shall thy light break forth as the morning, and thine health shall spring forth speedily." Isa. 58;8

*   *   *

Rather than thinking of ourselves as having bad habits of eating, or as being unable to control our obsession for food, let us remind ourselves that we have the Spirit of God in us. Surely this Spirit of God can take away our bad habits of eating, and enable us to control our overeating. We have the power to concentrate, to learn, to understand and to cope with all our problems, whether they be eating problems or other kinds. Every person has the Spirit of God in him. It is not taken by us, it is given to us at birth. All we need to do is call upon it. When we get this idea in our minds, we will be able to handle our emotions more efficiently. We can think and be able to concentrate more readily.

"We have the mind of Christ." 1 Cor. 2;16

*   *   *

How marvelous it is to feel free from compulsive overeating! How marvelous it is to be getting slimmer and slimmer each week! We are not so fearful or negative as we used to be. We are able to enjoy life and all others about us. We can stay in this state of feeling if we remember that we deserve happiness and goodness and we are worthy of success. We are not bound or limited in any way. Our declaration of faith will help to lift us quickly into an exalted state of mind and heart, a state in which we see above and beyond things that appear, a state in which we see ourselves thin, healthy, and happy, free from all the old compulsions for food.

"Men ought always to pray." Luke 18;1

I am calm, unhurried, and unafraid, for I am centered in the peace of God. I do not have to eat fattening foods because my calmness tells me that my body doesn't need them. I have a sense of Divine Order about my life and I can regulate myself to three moderate meals without craving certain kinds of foods. I can accomplish my work easily and on time, because I am spending less time eating. I put first things first. I get up in time to have a quiet time of prayer and reading to start my day. No matter what is before me to accomplish, this day I do the things I need to do easily and happily, without worry or anxiety if I have had my devotions each morning. I train myself to live in a peaceful, unhurried state of mind, I refuse to be excited by news in the paper, by the flurry of my family or friend's problems. I will not overeat when any disturbing situation comes to my attention. I bless all persons and all situations with a peaceful, poised, and undisturbed mind. My day moves along in an orderly manner as I tell myself often, "I am calm, serene, relaxed. I accomplish all things easily and on time, in a peaceful, unhurried state of mind."

"Great peace have they which love thy law; and nothing shall offend them." Psalms 119;165

* * *

I accept the truth that God is my guide, and I accept the truth that I must give up refined carbohydrates if I want to lose weight. I realize that I am not alone when I have to give up these foods. There are hundreds of persons who also can't assimilate them without gaining weight. God will give me the courage to be willing to understand and accept this fact about my body. I am glad and grateful that I know what things make me fat. All I have to do is eliminate them and I can lose weight. It is as simple as that, unless I want it to become difficult. I can hang on to my old cravings for sweets and starches if I remain unwilling to change my thinking and refuse to let God run my life. He will supply me with greater things than any food, and I am glad and grateful that I have His Divine Nature in me and He has given me the ability to stay on a proper eating plan. I am glad and grateful for all my many blessings of life. God knows my every need better than I know myself, and He needs me to express His love to others who can also be helped. He has given me special talents to use in fulfilling the best plan in my life. I trust Him to bless me with a happy, successful and wonderful life. I need not struggle or fight my need to lose weight but accept it gladly and be willing to do my share to reach the goal I desire.

"It is the Spirit himself bearing witness with our spirit that we are children of God." Rom. 8;16

*   *   *

Let us thank God, the source of our good, for all the ways in which we are guided to lose weight, and be helped. Let us thank Him for all the wonderful books that are written on diet and health, on emotions, and on spiritual help. Let us thank God for doctors who help patients to lose weight, or to get well. Let us thank God for spiriual leaders who also help others to understand themselves and God. Let us be thankful for all members of our family, our teachers of schools, and any acquaintances who have made our lives richer and more meaningful. Let us be thankful for all who have had a good influence upon our lives. Let us be thankful we are growing spiritually instead of fatter. Let us be thankful that when we need help and encouragement there is always someone to help us. God speaks through persons in many ways. We can be grateful for many things and persons.

"Giving thanks always for all things." Eph. 5;20

*   *   *

Success in weight loss depends largely on our ability to work with God. When we work with Him, we have a sense of doing things because we want to. We want to stay on our diet. We will eat only the foods which will help us lose. We will be enthusiastic about our new health plan instead of resenting it. We feel determined to achieve our goal. We are dedicated to accomplishing a weight loss; and we are certain to have good results because the fire of enthusiasm is burning in our hearts. Persistence always leads to the overcoming of every temptation and obstacle, for it will not let us give up or become discouraged. As we persist with enthusiasm and interest in doing the thing that is before us or constantly eating only the right foods, we find that we are replenished in power; that the power which pours through us to keep on eating right is God's own power flowing through us.

"It is good to be zealously affected always in a good thing." Gal. 4;18

*   *   *

I will keep in mind that my strength to lose weight must come from God, because I have failed so many times before when I depended upon my own "will power". When I rely on God, I can keep calm and not worry about failure, and I can be open to other good ideas that are necessary for my losing weight. I will have a secure feeling and be willing to give up all fattening foods as long as I trust Him to help me. My body will not lack anything, because all it really needs is protein, vegetables and some fruits in order to keep healthy and lose weight. I will cooperate with the ideas in this book and know my well-being is with me. Instead of lack, I will be in abundance and there is no limit to the wonderful foods I can eat which can also help me to lose weight. I will have success in many other ways as well, because I am open to new thoughts and ideas.

"Peace be within thy walls, and prosperity within thy palaces." Psalms 122;7

* * *

Divine Order — these two words contain spiritual power and bring help like magic. When you speak them, you are declaring the presence of God, the presence of good. You are preparing the way for the right outworking of every detail of your life, for the right handling of every situation. You are recognizing the truth about persons and situations and experiences. Many persons have used this idea of Divine Order to bless some situation in the home that needed improving or changed. We can use it for losing weight and giving up compulsive overeating. Others have used it in relation to their work, blessing themselves and whatever was before them with with the idea of Divine Order. It can become a good habit to declare Divine Order about any situation that calls for good judgment, wisdom and right handling. When you do not know how to proceed in some matter, where to turn, try starting with a declaration of Divine Order. It is surprising sometimes how quickly this declaration prepares the way for a smooth outworking of the details of daily living.

"Behold, I send my messenger." Matt. 11;10

* * *

To anyone who feels lonely, disillusioned; to anyone whose life is frustrated or disrupted; to anyone who longs to feel loved, who longs for happiness, who wants to lose weight; there is a way to find all things. If we long for happiness, we start to find it by making an effort — an effort to love. This may be a natural, easy thing for some persons, for others it seems difficult. Nevertheless, this is where we start. Let us reach out in loving thought to the persons around us — family, friends, or acquaintances — and think of them with love and appreciation. This alone will keep us from overeating. It is this feeling of appreciation that brings us close to other persons. Sometimes we need to appreciate ourselves as well as others, to know that we are God's children, that we are needed and important to Him. When we give expression to the love of God in our heart, we cannot help but stay on our diet and draw happy experiences to ourselves.

"For this is the message which you have heard from the beginning, that we should love one another." 1 John 3;11

*   *   *

We are constantly making choices and decisions. Whether to eat the fattening foods, or the best foods for our losing weight. From the moment we get out of bed, the need to choose and decide is thrust upon us. What clothing shall we wear? What food shall we eat? What action shall we take today? We even have to choose the thoughts we shall think. How good it is to start every day off right by asking God to direct and to guide us in making wise choices and right decisions. This willingness to ask for and accept God's help is a sign that we are willing to eat properly and be the person he wants us to be. To refuse to look to and accept His help would be as foolish as to refuse to breathe the life-giving air. If we habitually start our day by turning to God for guidance, in our eating and in all our affairs, our day will be blessed; we shall find life to be more and more satisfying.

"To give light to those who sit in darkness . . . to guide our feet into the way of peace." Luke 1;79

*   *   *

Each person's body is different from every other person's. He will find out which foods can help him lose weight and which make him gain. The decisions we make depend upon us and God, if we let Him help us. Sometimes we try to manage other person's diets or lives in some way that bothers them or ourselves. We must take care of our own problems and not be unduly concerned about those we cannot help. We can help others most when we free them to work out their lives for themselves. Say to yourself, "Today I will think before I give advice or try to manage anyone." As I think of something I believe another should do I will ask myself, "Is this my business?" My business, I know, is to follow God's directions for my life and to pray for others in the faith that they, too, are given inner guidance. I fully and freely release all persons to their highest good as God sees it, not as I with my limited vision see it. I listen and follow God's directions for me. That is all I need to do. I will eat what is right for my body and lose weight.

"This is the way, walk in it." Isa. 30;21

* * *

There are times when we need to forgive. It may be that we have a need to forgive ourselves. We may have a need to forgive a member of our family, a friend, a co-worker. We may need to forgive many persons. Sometimes the hardest person to forgive is ourselves. We judge ourselves harshly and have guilt feelings which we subconsciously try to punish by overeating and gaining weight. Once we feel worthy of losing weight, we will keep it off and give up the compulsion to overeat. We must accept ourselves as we are and go on from there. Nothing is too bad to forgive. Even after the worst binge of eating and gaining weight, we don't have to keep punishing ourselves further by feeling guilty. Forgiving ourselves right away is necessary, so we can continue our weight loss program. As we pray in the Divine Order we will be able to forgive and have an understanding heart. When we understand why we do the things we do, why we fail to do the things we should do, we will more easily forgive ourselves. When we understand the motives and pressures in the lives of others, we will want to forgive them. When we understand the needs, the longings, the hopes of the whole human race, we will work to express the same forgiving love that God relates to us.

"Forgive, and you will be forgiven." Luke 6;37

* * *

Some of us compulsive overeaters have been negative people for so long that we automatically get negative about every new thought or idea. We are constantly speaking words, and feeling certain emotions. Why not make them positive words, productive of good? Why not eat right and act right and give ourselves credit for the good in us? Why not give ourselves a little praise? This body of ours is going to be an attractive one. It was born beautiful and worked efficiently and it can be that way again. The body is quite responsive to thought and word. Let us consider the work our body is doing for us without our conscious direction, and then let us praise its every organ and every function. Our ears hear, our hearts beat, our arms move, our legs walk, our minds think, our noses smell, our tongues taste, and all our organs function properly if we give them the best of care. Our body is blessed with life and strength and health.

"Let the words of my mouth . . . be acceptable in thy sight." Psalms 19;14

*   *   *

There may be appearances of injustice in my life, it may seem that my good is being withheld from me, or that someone or something is depriving me of that which is rightfully mine. I am determined not to "eat about it". I now lift my thoughts above the appearance, I deny any belief in injustice. I affirm that God's law is an unfailing law of love and justice, that in Him there is divine balance, divine give-and-take. And I know, too, that my own good is established forever in God; that it cannot be withheld from me, that it comes to me surely, swiftly, without hindrance or delay. I expect to be treated fairly and justly; I know that God is at work in all persons and in all situations to bring about that which is right and just for all. I give thanks that all things are working together for my highest good and for the highest good of all concerned. My mind is at peace, for I have let go of fear and resentment. My trust is in God.

"Blessed is the man who trusts in the Lord." Jer. 17;7

*   *   *

When we are overweight and have to hurry or run, we get out of breath very fast. We must pause and rest. When we work, we cannot keep going very long without getting tired. We surely know that if we lose some excess weight our bodies will function better. We will gladly diet and lose weight in order to be more comfortable and have more energy. Sometimes we rebel at staying away from fattening foods, but it will pay off in the long run and we will be so happy later that we will wonder how we could have ever let food become so important in our lives. If life appears to be without meaning, if we are discouraged, downhearted, confused, frightened, let us consider God's love for us. Let us allow Him to help us to eat the right foods and refresh us with His spirit. Let us take time to turn to Him in prayer when we get tempted and go on a binge. When we get back on our diet, it is like coming home to a safe place again. In returning we will rediscover the stability, the poise, the courage God gave to us in the very beginning.

"In returning and rest you shall be saved." Isa. 30;15

It is difficult for many of us to be kind to ourselves. We condemn ourselves much more severely than we would anyone else. Often, too, we go over and over in our minds incidents in which we did not act as we wish we had. Especially when we overeat or eat some fattening food we blame ourselves and feel guilty. We can be free from self-condemnation. We free ourselves by refusing to think harshly about anything we may have done. We know better now, because that kind of thinking does us no good. When thoughts of the past come, we say, "That is over. I learned from it. God now makes it right for everyone concerned. I see myself as God sees me. I see myself as expressing all the qualities of God within me and I am free. I am worthy of God's love and I am worthy of a trim body and normal weight. As I let go of the past, and as I quit condemning myself, I open the way for new good to enter my life. My burden is set down, and I am ready to receive the good God has for me now.

"Beloved, if our hearts do not condemn us, we have confidence before God; and we receive from him whatever we ask." 1 John 3;21,22

* * *

What kind of thoughts are you thinking? Do you want to eat the wrong foods? Do you hate someone? Are you holding a grudge? Our thoughts are more important than most of us realize, for they govern our feelings and actions. If we do not have the kind of lives we long for, let us look to our thinking and feeling. We may discover that we have been allowing ourselves to be negative in our approach to life. But we have control over our minds; we have the power to change our thoughts and feelings. If you find yourself thinking or reacting by eating in a negative way, even in a small matter, stop right then and declare the truth, the truth about yourself, the truth about the situation, the truth about other persons. You declare the truth by putting the substance in your thought, the weight of your spiritual authority on the side of good. You bless, rather than condemn; you give thanks, rather than complain; you express faith, rather than doubt; you think in terms of health, slimness, happiness, and success.

"As he (man) thinketh in his heart, so is he." Prov. 23;7

* * *

I don't have to hold any unhealthy or negative thought about my overweight problem by accepting it as something inherited. All I really inherited was my family's appetite. The fat is caused from overeating and I must face the truth. I can do something about that. I don't have to say, "This overweight problem runs in my family."

It is not a disease that is inherited, but caught by bad habits. My weak ness to crave sweets and starches was handed down to me by others but I don't have to accept it. If I have already accepted it, I can ge rid of it by changing my fat thinking to healthful thinking. My at titude about food depends on how much it means to me. I am a chil of God, and I am composed of the very substance of God. There i a pattern of perfection in me that can emerge as I let God's idea take over in me. I can think of myself as putting on the perfection o Him — mentally, physically, and emotionally, besides spiritually. think of myself first as a spiritual being, having a body of goodness I think of every cell in my body as filled with His light, and I thinl of myself as free from limitation of any kind; free to express healtl and wholeness; free to give up compulsive eating; free to expres God's goodness, and be in His image as the person He created.

"Your whole body will be full of light." Matt. 6;22

*   *   *

What we actually experience moment by moment is our inner lif(of emotions, attitudes, responses, and thoughts. When our inner lif(is harmonious and orderly, filled with love and peace, we are happy and fulfilled no matter what the outward experience may be. We may want to overeat at times, but we will be filled with so much good that we will stop craving to eat. Hunger pangs will not come so often and as we relax we can go many hours without even thinking about food. When we outwardly pretend everything is going well, we will still get hungry for food, unless our inner life is free from negative thoughts. We still experience a lack in our lives when we try to cover up our feelings about something or someone. We must keep our inner life centered in the spirit of God until it becomes as a garden of loveliness and beauty expressed in our whole being. One who has the Divine Spirit is not going to harbor resentments and secret criti-cisms for very long. He does not allow his mind to wander over meaningless things; he is aware instantly when any false belief takes hold of his mind, and he is able to correct it without eating. As we keep our inner life centered in the integrity of God's spirit, only goodness can pervade our mind, body, and affairs.

"As for me, I walk in my integrity." Psalms 26;11

*   *   *

Often the greatest help we receive comes through affirming the simplest of words, such as "I let go, I let God." Yet nothing is more important to our personal, spiritual freedom than letting go and letting

God. Letting go of our fears lifts us in faith; letting go of our needs and letting God show us the way of fulfillment brings forth blessings in our lives. We need to remember that God does not do things for us, but He acts through us. He cannot make us stay on a diet, but His spirit in us can be a reminder to eat what is best for us. As we let go of less important things such as desires for certain foods, and let His presence and power work through us, we will be able to lose weight more steadily. When we let God's life be in charge of our body temple, it functions perfectly. When we let His substance be active in us, our life prospers in creative, productive ways. As we let God's love take hold of our emotional nature, we are able to relate to others harmoniously and this will enable us to eat less. By letting go and letting God, we release our tense hold on things and allow room for the life, substance and love of God to work through us and our affairs.

"The branch cannot bear fruit by itself." John 15;4

* * *

It is a good thing that we cannot foretell what is going to happen. We cannot progress that way. Life comes to us day by day and we can only see and live it a little at a time. We do not want to dwell in the past — on the times when we felt a sense of failure in some area of life, or even on the times that were filled with exceptional happiness. We can bless and release all that has been in the past, for we handled that moment of life to the best of our ability at that time. All that is yet to come, we can bless and release too, for we will handle that moment of life to the best of our ability when that time comes. Sometimes we get negative thoughts and think we can't lose any more than a certain number of pounds. We say, "I always do such and so." This is not good, because it plants a thought in our mind that we cannot change. We should say, "I used to do such and so, but now with God's help I am able to do this and that, and many other things I have never done before." All that is to come we can bless and release to God, for we will handle that moment of life to the best of our ability when that time comes. Now is the moment, the moment to do God's will. As we attune ourselves to His will, we are able to make wise use of today. We handle our eating and all of today's problems under His direction. Today we rejoice in and fulfill our divine purpose.

"We are God's children now." 1 John 3;2

New Year's Day: At the beginning of the year how easy it seem to make a new start! As the old year passes into the new we automatically think of events of last year and things which have passed away. We naturally tend toward newness — new ideas — new beginnings. We may have failed to lose weight last year, but we are more determined to do so in the coming year. We must consider how we are going to change in order to accomplish this goal. If we carry the feeling of willingness to change with us each day, we can lose weight this coming year. We can experience the joy of being a new person. Each day will bring new opportunities to feel free from the past hurts. As we live in the assurance of God's love and presence in us, moment by moment, we will be rewarded with a whole new life.

"Therefore if any one is in Christ, he is a new creation; the old has passed away, behold, the new has come." 2nd, Corin. 5;17

* * *

Now that this book has told me clearly what to eat — what to do in order to lose weight — and to accept God's help — I have no more need to put off my losing this weight which burdens me so much. There are no more excuses. No longer do I have to be afraid of the future or fear to act on the faith I need to guide me. I am constantly in the process of *what to eat* and foods *not to eat* and I will find value in this concept. I will open my mind to healthful foods, so I can be sure of losing the weight I need to lose. I can do this with God's help.

"You are the light of the world." Matt. 5;14

* * *

When you allow yourself to become angry or upset, you immediately get hunger pangs and want to eat something. It is usually something sweet or starchy that you crave for comfort. Why? That is your nature. It could be drugs, alcohol or something worse. But your compulsive personality chose food. Now that you know this, don't give in to it. You can control these desires for compulsive eating by reading some parts of this book or praying or calling someone and talking out how you feel. You can learn to hold steady in the center of emotions even if you do feel hungry. Hunger pangs are not always what we think they are. As we practice keeping ourselves God centered it will become easier to stay away from compulsive eating. It will help us to a calmness, guiltlessness and steadiness of spirit so that we can meet all things undisturbed and with inner assurance.

"He maketh the storm a calm, so that the waves thereof are still." Psalms 107;29

Communication is an important word. It is at the heart of prayer. It is a way in which we reach God and a way in which He reaches us. People can also communicate and reach each other by talking, trying to understand, and learn from each other. Some of us are compulsive talkers and we seldom listen. Some listen, but do not contribute their thoughts or ideas. True communication consists of both talking and listening. We need to express ourselves, to say what is in our minds and hearts, and we need to be able to listen with understanding, interest, insight and appreciation. Let us keep the lines of communication open between ourselves and the new ideas presented in this book.

"Yet their voice goes out through all the earth." Psalms 19;4

*   *   *

What can we do when a situation is impossible to change? One thing we should not do is "eat about it". That does absolutely no good. If a situation involves another person we hesitate to take a stand, because it might hurt someone's feelings. It may be a state of affairs that has lasted so long that we have come to take it for granted — we think there is nothing we can do — now to change it. But we can always do something about every situation. We can pray for wisdom. God works through us and we need to be open to new ideas. His power enables us to meet situations which we are usually unable to meet. We can overcome many problems just by prayer. We can look past our appearance of fat and make the right decision to lose and the right foods to eat. We can proceed and change our whole being.

"With God all things are possible." Matt. 19;26

*   *   *

I shall not fear going on a diet. I shall not fear losing weight. I shall not fear peoples' criticism. I shall not fear their influence on me to get me to eat fattening foods. Wherever I am and wherever I go I shall stand firm on my idea to lose weight and keep it off. I know God is with me wherever I go and whatever I do. I shall not fear this change in my life as I know that I am doing what is best for my health and happiness.

"Underneath are the everlasting arms." Deut. 33;27

*   *   *

Do I really want to lose weight for myself and keep it off? Do I want to experience a change in my whole life? Am I willing to think differently about food? I am in charge of my thoughts and words, and with God's loving help I can make them positive and constructive. I will give my mind to thoughts of health, strength and freedom from compulsive eating. I will put these ideas into action Is there a lack in my life? Instead of talking and thinking about my need, I will supply the good actions which are presented to me. will give thanks for these new ideas. I will quit thinking about my lack and conform to the good I will experience from giving up fat tening foods.

"As he (man) thinketh in himself, so is he." Prov. 23;7

*   *   *

We can gain strength of our body by eating properly. We can get strength of our mind by reading good books. We can get strength of our spirit by prayer. We can challenge ourselves each day to add new strength in all these areas. With God's help we can become a whole person full of many strengths. We will be strong enough to be kind instead of unkind. We can be strong enough to be tolerant instead of prejudiced. We can be gentle to others instead of harsh. We can abstain from overeating instead of indulging. Whatever our need for strength may be, we can find the strength through God. He is our strength. We can meet any challenge and overcome any experience to make a change. God is with us and gives us strength at all times.

"On the day I called, thou didst answer me, my strength of soul thou didst increase." Psalms 138;3

*   *   *

Can we maintain a loving, friendly, forgiving spirit and still obtain justice? This is a question that bothers many. To hold onto a belief that one must be unforgiving, that he must hang on to bitterness and resentment in order to defend himself from injustice is one reason why some people continue to overeat. True justice is based on the law of love. So the more we are able to keep in tune with this law of love, the more we are assured of justice in our life. We know that the more we empty our hearts of bitterness and resentment, the closer we feel to God and the less we'll need to turn to food. The more we are able to express love and forgiveness, the greater sense of freedom and inner power we feel. God's power is at work to adjust every condition.

"His banner over me was love." Song of Sol. 2;4

God has placed within each of us the potential for success and prosperity. In every person is that special talent, that special gift he has to give to the world, which will prosper and bless him as he gives expression to it. No one is left out; each one is vitally important to God in the scheme of things. No one else can give to the world that which you have been uniquely created to give. When we realize we are special and have something that we alone can give to life, it is easy to be convinced and we can act on these thoughts. We are meant to be full of enthusiasm and unique creativeness.

"Do not neglect the gift you have." 1 Tim. 4;14

*　　*　　*

Whenever an overweight person makes a decision to lose weight, he gets a new power from within, and a new perspective and a new drive to better himself in all ways of life. When he commits himself to lose weight he must also commit himself to God's will. Here is the source of his success. God can help us to live a more constructive life and he will give us divine energy to stay on our proper eating plan. When we choose mostly proteins and vegetables as our diet, we can have the assurance of steady weight loss. Let us commit ourselves to a constructive plan for each day and approach it unfailingly.

"When a man vows a vow to the Lord . . . he shall not break his word; he shall do according to all that proceeds out of his mouth." Num. 30;2

*　　*　　*

Oftentimes food controls us when we should be in control of it. This is where we need God's help. We can always choose our own response to fattening foods. We can fear eating them or we can be unafraid and ignore them. By doing the right thing for our bodies, we can like ourselves more each day. We can become willing to react differently when these foods appear in front of us. How we respond is how we are going to act and either lose weight or gain it. We can bring the best to our lives by changing our attitude about how good they taste. Taste means nothing after the food is eaten. The food remains inside us unused and turns to fat. If we dominate our desires we have an inner peace and power. Our success is whether we let God help us or keep trying to do it alone.

"He that covereth his sins, shall not prosper; but whoso confesseth and forsaketh shall have mercy." Psalms 28;13

Patience is a positive quality. When we have patience with ourselves in this business of losing weight we can keep on the right track. We must not blame ourselves and give up. We can keep trying no matter how much we fail. Each time we try we strengthen ourselves more. It is a good process and a definite part of our spiritual growth. Patience with ourselves, and others, and all of life, makes it possible for us to keep trying until we are strengthened so that we may continue to walk in the right and divine order of things.

"Now the God of patience and consolation grant you to be like minded one toward another, according to Christ Jesus." Rom. 15;5

* * *

Make me a new person, O God. Let my old thoughts about food, my old aches and pains be released and remembered no more. Fill me through Your power with a new and restored life. Give me courage to diet and give up my craving for sweets and starches. Fill me with a newness so I won't desire these foods. Give me a new will to live and a new response to life. Let me be vitally alive and energetic. God, move through me, live through me, think through me. Let my spirit be high and going forward to new heights. God, bless me in this new life.

"Then shall your light break forth like the dawn, and your healing shall spring up steadily." Isa. 58;8

* * *

One of the most refreshing things I can do is take all my old bad habits and everything that concerns me to God and to realize that He will perfect all my emotions and affairs. God is the love which harmonizes the most twisted emotions and as compulsive overeaters, we are pretty mixed up emotionally sometimes. He can resolve all our conflicts. As God becomes active in me I can lose weight and give up old cravings for certain foods. I will give all these old needs into His loving care. I visualize my mind free from their cravings and desires. I visualize myself slim and healthy. Whenever I get tempted I'll say, "God is perfecting me and I needn't be concerned with these foods."

"The Lord will perfect that which concerneth me." Psalms 38;8

* * *

When the challenge to lose weight presents itself to us, we may be fearful because the new way of eating is different. This is understandable. But remembering that God is with us enables us to meet this new change and meet it well and willingly. We can help ourselves even more if we find someone else who is trying to lose weight. We can give ourselves and that person help, just by discussing our common problem. We can get and receive encouragement because we will realize we are negative in our dilemma. There are thousands of unhappy overweight people seeking security and love to help themselves stop compulsive overeating.

"They shall be safe." Ezek. 34;27

*　　*　　*

Some of us have had bad experiences in our religious lives. Some of us had parents who made religion one of fear and unhappiness. Some of us had unfortunate relationships with either the priest, minister, rabbi, or some member of the church. We must remember just because one or two persons makes our experience in a church unhappy we should not quit trying to get something from religion. We can go to another church or pray in groups of different kinds and we can always have a devotional life by ourselves or with our families. A spiritual life of some kind is necessary for all overeaters, because they are very much in need of a Higher Power to help them.

"For where two or three are gathered together in my name, there I am in the midst of them." Matt. 18;20

*　　*　　*

When someone near and dear to us is in need of help, we may try in every way we know to give him the help we think he needs. Sometimes we are unable to meet his demands. Sometimes he rejects our attempts to help him. Let us first pray for guidance to do and act in the best way possible. Then we must have patience and keep calm and wait for God's love to work through that person or situation. In the waiting period we give thanks for the insight which will come to us as we pray and have faith. We can have the assurance that a calm faith will bring victory.

"We with patience wait." Rom. 8;25

*　　*　　*

We can be steady in our proper eating habits — not dieting one day and "bingeing" the next. This is no way to slimness or lasting peace with ourselves. We must be steady and confident each day as we strive to live right, eat right, and enable ourselves to gradually lose weight. We will hold onto our faith and have the conviction that what we are doing is best for us. We shall find it easy to keep our thinking positive and optimistic, because we know that God's spirit is with us. We will not fear others who tempt us to eat fattening foods. *"Follow me."* Matt. 16;24

*   *   *

This is a day to be glad we are alive. We have found a way to lose weight and a new joy in our lives. The answers are here in this book if we only accept them and use them. We can now rise above all the desires to overeat that we used to have. We can be what we are meant to be. We can rejoice in God's love and His tremendous power at work in our minds and hearts and lives. This is a day to rejoice and be happy. We are free from foods which bound us. We have come to a new understanding of ourselves. This feeling will be for each day and each moment.

"I shall again praise Him, my help and my God." Psalms 42;5

*   *   *

Let us continue in our overcoming the desire for too many sweets and starches. The longer we resist them, the less important they become. The more weight we lose, the happier we'll be. The loss of pounds is worth the sacrifice of foods. God's love will keep us strong on our new way of life and He will guide us daily so we will not fail.

"I am the light of the world." John 8;12

*   *   *

I have a power within me to stop overeating compulsively. This power will lift me out of depression and guilt and give me a new vision of myself as slim and healthy. The past is gone, I no longer have to be fat. The new spirit is changing me each day. I see clearly now that my past need for foods did me no good, but harm. The results of what I eat shows up on my body. The source of my trim body must come from protein, vegetables, and fruits. As I study and realize it and believe this, I open the way for success and supply for my every need."

"It will be given to you; good measure pressed down, shaken together, running over." Luke 6;38

*   *   *

As I pray for guidance, I will act on ideas that come to me. New ideas will come and I shall not dismiss them. Ideas can come from others, books, or myself. God speaks through these ways as I seek answers for better living. If a persistent feeling keeps telling me to change some area in my life, I shall do it. This is God pointing the way and showing me a course of action. The more I pray, the more I keep my mind open to receive guidance of His spirit, the more readily I will be able to follow through and act on it.

"I will instruct you and teach you in the way you should go; I will counsel you with my eyes upon you." Psalms 32;8

*   *   *

When we overeat and gain weight what do we want to do? We want to stop eating and lose weight. We want to change, but we can't! Only God can help us. We can make it easier for ourselves to change by changing our thoughts about food. We can see ourselves as we really are. Putting too much thought on our desires instead of our needs. We can look at our true selves and know that we really don't want to overeat. This is just an escape from our real needs which we cannot meet. Now we know we need God. There is no doubt any more so we will seek His way for us. We will lift up our thoughts to goodness, and peace will come as we strive to live right.

"There is therefore no condemnation for those who are in Christ Jesus." Rom. 8;1

*   *   *

I need never feel lonely, unloved, or without a purpose for living. I am a child of God, and right where I am, I am needed and important to Him. God's divine purposes are being fulfilled in me. I believe this and believe He will see me through. God needs me to express His love and joy so that my desire to be accepted and approved of, is the spirit of God in me. I must give to others in order to receive. This is the way to a full new life. God needs me as a channel through which His blessing and peace and understanding can be poured out to all I meet.

"See what the love of the Father has given us, that we should be called the children of God." 1 John 3;1

*   *   *

When we see others eat refined carbohydrates and not gain weight, we may feel that this is unjust. Perhaps right in our own home others eat these fattening foods, even large amounts of them and don't gain weight. It seems so unfair. All we can do is face the fact that our bodies "can't afford them." Don't keep feeling deprived. Actually these foods are not very healthful for even a slim person, so why are you feeling so sorry about giving them up? Our attitude about the whole matter is the only thing we need to change, then our giving them up won't seem so unjust. We can reestablish ourselves in the assurance that God loves us, and He wants us to eat healthful foods and this will help us lose weight. We have no prejudice against other people who are different from us.

"Blessed are the peacemakers, for they shall be called the sons of God." Matt. 5;9

* * *

Love is the complete answer to all life's problems. If we love ourselves properly we won't want to damage our bodies by overeating. We will want to share our love and knowledge with others who have the same problems. Love and understanding are the great needs of everyone, we shall always be able to give a blessing when we feel love. Even a silent prayer for someone is a powerful help. As we let our thoughts and feelings motivate in love our actions will respond to what is good and best for our lives. We'll find a peace and happiness never known before in each situation of life we experience.

"By this all men will know that you are my disciples, if you have love for one another." John 13;35

* * *

I say to my mind, "Today I'll eat right. You don't need food for comfort. God can give you all the comfort you need. I will think clearly and get intelligence enough to stay on my diet so I can be at peace with myself." I will say to my emotions "Peace Be Still". This will give me an inner stillness and quietness. I acknowledge God at work in me and my emotions. My feelings will be in perfect control as I respond to all conditions and people with the warmth of love and cheerfulness. My relationships with others will be harmonious and I know that love and order are at work.

"Be still and know that I am God." Psalms 46;10

* * *

If ever we get tempted to eat because we are alone or discouraged, we have the power to get rid of the feeling quickly. All we have to do is be thankful to God for the good feelings we do have. We can thank God for His presence in us and the fact that we are never alone. His presence can bring action and a renewed spirit to our lives. All the good we need is present in us; we only need to realize this and we can be lifted up to a new life.

"Underneath are the everlasting arms." Deut. 33;27

Most of us overeaters turn to food when something annoys us. We get upset or disturbed out of all proportion to their importance. Many of us have found it helps to say to ourselves, "I refuse to eat about this or be upset. I know God will see me through." Try saying this each time you are tempted to eat when you give way to irritation, frustration or annoyance. Things do not always go according to schedule; sometimes we find ourselves waiting impatiently for someone or we may be doing something important to us and get interrupted by someone who doesn't care. This may sound trivial, but if we get upset it is not trivial. Our good health and peace of mind and well being are affected by the way we react to the daily happenings. An undisturbed mind can be with us as we let God enter our lives.

"I will put my laws into their minds." Heb. 8;10

* * *

There is no fat person who cannot lose weight. Faith and action are all it takes to lose weight and keep it off. Most overweight persons can lose 10 pounds in a month if they stay away from refined carbohydrates. This can mean 120 pounds a year for some who get a spiritual awakening from God and His power goes to work each day, never failing. 10 pounds a month is only 2½ pounds a week. This is a good amount to lose. It can be done. Others have done it and so can you — with God's help. You can't do it alone — so don't try. As you release all your concerns and fears to God, He will take complete charge of your mind and body, making it a joy to lose weight. Give thanks that God's powerful spirit is in you waiting to be called upon.

"The power of the Lord was with him to heal." Luke 5;17

* * *

Each persons body is unique and different. Some people can lose weight easier than others. The persons who are relaxed can lose easier than the ones who become too anxious about dieting. There is something about the calmness that allows the body to function properly so it will use up more calories. As we relax we will become amazed and grateful for each daily victory. We need to cease resentments or resistance towards anyone, no matter how difficult he may be, or what our relationship to him has become. A friendly outgoing warm regard for all people enables us to lose weight and also know others have good in them. We can be open to what is beneath the surface and respond to people with care for them.

"A friend loves at all times." Prov. 17;17

If we have been burdened with a thought of being unjustly mistreated, or if we have been disturbed because of the appearance of others we are not relying on God. Our lives and the lives of others are always in God's care. To know this should release any anxiety about them; it is to think of them as God's children; it is to think of them as being directed and protected in all ways. It is not always easy to release our feelings of anxiety about someone, but in doing so we often find our freer, more confident attitude opens the way for communication and understanding between us. We cannot protect, or shield others, but we can bless them and trust God to direct them.

"He will give his angels charge of you to guard you in all your ways." Psalms 91;11

* * *

Would you like to take part in an experiment? Would you like to see how many things you can find to give thanks for today? As you go about your daily task, stop and write down some person, some thing, some courtesy received, some thoughtfullness expressed, that you have been taking for granted. Now is the time to give thanks. You will find time all day long to give thanks audibly and silently. You will have a new awareness and discover many ways to give thanks. This will enable you to think of more important things than food. This will enable you to think about more inspirational things, so it can become a new way of life for you.

"Always and for everything giving thanks in the name of our Lord Jesus Christ to God the Father." Eph. 5;20

* * *

When we say aloud "God Bless you" we can sincerely feel this power. We can try saying this when someone seems unfair to us. This prayer helps us to remember that the way to justice and order is through blessing and not through anger. When we say "God Bless you" we are asking God to pour out the blessing of harmony and love that heals every misunderstanding. When we feel close to someone and say "God Bless you" these words bring both that person and us in a bond of unity and love. This power of blessing can be used any time and any place, under any circumstance. Saying, "God Bless you" conveys love, good will, and a desire to work harmoniously.

"Bless those who persecute you; bless and do not curse them . . . Live in harmony with one another." Rom. 12;14-16

God is with me, filling me with a new spirit. I refuse to give way to self-pity. I refuse to remain cast down or sad. I lift up my eyes; I lift up my head; I lift up my thoughts. I am willing to find happiness in the present. I will not mourn the past; I will not look back on happier days. Here where I am, God is — good is — blessings are. I know this and nothing that happens is going to make me over-eat. Every change in my life will be met with serenity and acceptance because God will help me to handle each problem. He will not fail me for I will open up my heart and mind for new blessings to enter in. I open my life for a great goodness that will come. Always a better way is open before me.

"To thee, O Lord, I lift up my soul O my God, in Thee I trust." Psalms 25;1

*   *   *

Many times we wish we had lots of money so we could be able to give lavishly to all we know and love. But what we want from other persons are not expensive gifts. We want love, approval, faith, the encouragement, and friendship of others. And this is what others want from us. More than any outer gift, the gift we can give to others is the gift of ourselves. It has been said, that the gift without the giver is bare. When we give ourselves to others, we give to them the very substance of our thoughts, the very depth of our love, the very spirit of our faith. Today as we think of others in our life, let us give them the gift of our prayers, the gift of our faith, the gift of our selves and the gift of our loving appreciation. These are rich gifts that all of us can give.

"Silver and gold have I none; but such as I have give I thee." Acts 3;6

*   *   *

Christmastime — is the time for giving and receiving. There is a Bible verse which says, "It is more blessed to give than to receive." Sometimes we find it harder to receive from others than give to them. Some persons cannot accept gifts graciously, who by their reluctance to be on the receiving end, spoil the joy of the one who wants to give. During the Christmas season we all think of giving and receiving. We want to share with others and express our love and appreciation and bring happiness to others by giving gifts. But we must remember that joy of receiving is also important. Let us express a spirit of appreciation and enthusiasm for every gift and every blessing. Christmas time is not the time to overeat; even if man has seemed to make it that way.

Jesus would not want us to celebrate his birth by our overeating and gaining weight. Do we want to celebrate this way?

"Always and forevr giving thanks." Eph. 5;20

*   *   *

There is nothing that God's love cannot harmonize and adjust Some are hesitant to pray for such things as health, overweight, compulsive eating, sex problems, financial problems, divorce problems, fears of death and many other problems. These are the biggest problems and the closest to us and yet we refuse to pray about them. Why? We need to talk to God about them. He knows already, so why not talk to Him about them? His love is ever present in every situation and circumstance, waiting to be recognized. Prayer opens our inner thoughts to love and harmony and brings love and harmony into expression. No matter how bad a particular situation has become, a prayer charged with thoughts of good will and feelings of love will bring forth the right and perfect answer. If it is some particular person bothering you pray with this thought, "With thoughts of good will and feelings of love, I pray for you." It may not be easy at first to bless someone who has been a challenge to us; but we can always turn to God and bring that person into our prayers. Gradually we will begin to feel a closeness of God's love and real thoughts of blessing and love will come into our minds for each one for whom we pray. Then our prayers will be powerful and effective.

"We always pray for you." 2nd. Thess. 1;11

*   *   *

We want things in our life to work out harmoniously and we want to lose weight. We want to go along each day without friction or fuss. We want a divine order in our lives. The new disciplined eating plan can become so powerful in our daily lives that it will become our first reaction. To eat right — live right — think right, we are making gradual changes to improve daily. We are learning new thoughts about accepting ourselves and others. All things good fall into place according to the best plans and schedules, if we ask God to guide us. When we admit we need His help and humble ourselves God becomes active in all our affairs.

"Commit your way to the Lord; trust in him, and he will act." Psalms 37;5

*   *   *

There is no situation that is too difficult for a solution. The power of God in us. No matter how fat we are now, we can lose weight and keep it off — if and "if" is a little word with a big meaning — if we depend upon God instead of ourselves. The power of God is in everyone. Some people use it and some don't. It is our decision to use it now. There will be new ways opened up so we can eat without craving more. We will be able to sit down at a meal, relaxed and able to slowly chew the proper foods we need to help us to slimness. The power of God is always in us, but we are the ones who activate it, who call it forth in the experiences we meet from day to day. As I turn to God for help, I lay aside all my desires for fattening foods; tension, stress, and other anxieties will fade away. These unhealthful cravings will not bother me so much any more. I will release them in prayer and find freedom in myself. I will let God's presence settle within me and I will relax so I won't need sweets or starches. Nothing from within can make me crave them for I have a new peace. I trust Him to make my way easier, happier and harmonious. I know that with Him, my diet will be accepted calmly and I will be at peace and have a serene atmosphere about my life, and shall lose weight.

"Behold, I am with you and will keep you wherever you go." Gen. 28;15

*   *   *

I am going to try a new eating plan of healthful foods and I am going to be challenged to stick to it. I can then be certain of losing weight. I can have assurance when I ask God to help me. He will help me be honest in my eating. I am going to write down anything I eat before I eat in order to keep honest with myself and Him. He is always with me, to guide me if I let Him. I am looking forward with happy anticipation to a trim, healthful body and a new, wonderful life. I will always go with God as my guide. It will be safe, easy, happy, and successful if I depend on His spirit to guide me. His love will give me confidence to eat and live right. Nothing is too hard for me to do with His help. His good awaits me.

"Behold, I am with you and will keep you wherever you go." Gen. 28;15

*   *   *

Regardless of the negative thoughts you have about yourself you are good. You are made up of God's mind, body and spirit and His love. Look at yourself as an expression of God, the good. This is your true identity. So if you are fat and overweight, this does not mean that you are going to continue that way. Visualize and feel the change that is taking place. Cleanse your mind of self-criticism. It is not hard to find goodness in oneself — you only need to look for it. You can change your condition by develping the attitude that easily finds the good. Do not feel that it is hard to know God. God is the love that gives you all the things of life and your very being. Give thanks for your own ability to find good, then the transforming and changing will easily take place in your life.

"The wisdom that is from above, is first pure, then peaceable, gentle, and easy to be entreated." James 3;17

FOOD FOR THOUGHT
Meditations and Prayers

The following section is one of the most important in this book. It is the salvation and answer to the overeater's dilemma and will arrest or cure the "disease" of craving for refined carbohydrates. It must be read, studied, and believed every day, so it will become a part of the reader's daily thinking and life. None of it should be taken lightly. The ideas for the "Food For Thought" (meditations and prayers) section were taken from persons who wish to remain anonymous, and I am grateful for the use of them.

* * *

I am an unhappy person. I have gained weight and am willing to do anything to get my self-respect. I am so sick of my way of living and overeating that I can't stand myself.

In this new year I will live one day at a time. I will make each new day one of preparation for better things ahead. I will not dwell on the past or future, only the present. I will try to get rid of all thoughts of unkindness, all my dislikes, my resentments, my sense of failure, my disappointments in others and in myself. I will leave the past and go forward in this new year into a new life.

Am I really ready to stay on a diet?

PRAYER: *I pray that God will guide me into proper eating habits one day at a time — one meal at a time. I pray He will help me from snacking in-between meals.*

* * *

Now that I have resolved to change my way of living to a better one, I must admit I am helpless, that sweets and starches had me hooked and I couldn't stop eating too much of them. The next thing is to take action and honestly be willing to give them up entirely. I must quit that old habit of compulsive overeating. I must surrender my life to a Higher Power, put my eating problem into His hands and leave it there. Man can only carry the burden of 24 hours, no more. Many times he weighs himself down with the years behind and the days that haven't come. He gets upset and realizes he can't do a thing about either of these times. We should not be so foolish as to keep gathering up burdens of the past, because we need God to help us forgive, bear, or forget the past. Count your blessings just for today and forget past hurts.

PRAYER: *I pray that I may realize that my past experiences are behind me and I don't have to keep experiencing them over again. I must face this next 24 hours with hope and courage.*

* * *

I realize finally that I am a compulsive overeater. I admit it openly to myself, to God, and to another person before I can recover. I must read books which will help me to a healthier, happier life. Am I willing to apply these beneficial books to my life?

I will be renewed. I will be remade. In this I need God's help. His spirit will flow in me and shall sweep away all my desire to overeat. Each day I will improve my life in some way. I shall try to keep living the way I believe God wants me to.

Am I ready to admit it and seek help?

PRAYER: *I pray that I may be taught by listening and taking other's suggestions. I pray that I may try new ideas and experience a new way of eating and living and accept them gladly.*

* * *

Have I admitted I am a compulsive overeater or do I still try to eat these so called goodies like normal eaters eat? Have I swallowed my pride and admitted I am different from normal eaters? Have I accepted the fact that I must spend the rest of my life without my binge foods? Have I any reservations in the back of my mind that someday I'll be able to eat like a normal person? Am I absolutely honest with myself and others? Have I taken an inventory of myself and admitted the wrongs I have done?

I will believe that basically I am a good person. Good things will happen to me. I believe God cares for me and will provide for me and I will not plan too far ahead. He expects me to carry only one day's experience at a time.

Have I tried to make up to others for the way I have treated them?

PRAYER: *I pray that I may not worry about other's problems. I pray that I can take care and correct my own problems.*

* * *

Have I turned to a Higher Power for help? Do I believe that each person I see whom I admire is a demonstration of God, to help change me into a useful citizen? Am I living one day at a time?

I believe God's presence brings peace and will clean all my irritations away if I let Him. I can rest my nerves and not be afraid. I will learn how to relax and not need food to anesthetize my body. When I am relaxed, God's strength can flow into me and I can then have peace.

Do I ask God to give me the power to stay on a diet for each 24 hours?

PRAYER: *I pray for peace to understand myself better. I pray for guidance to a better life.*

* * *

Keeping on a proper eating plan is the most important thing in my life. The most important decision I've made is to give up compulsive overeating.

I am convinced that my whole life depends on not taking that first bite between meals. Nothing in the world is as important to me as my staying away from the wrong foods. Everything, my whole life depends on my keeping strong.

I will discipline myself today and now. I will turn out all thought of overeating and realize that the good actions in my life are necessary for my well being. I will welcome hunger pangs as a sign of losing weight. I can gain strength to accept them from God as He can give me the strength to abstain.

Can I afford to give in once in awhile for just a few bites?

PRAYER: *I pray that I may face and accept whatever discipline is necessary. I pray that God will guide me and give me power to give up compulsive eating.*

* * *

When temptation comes as it does sometimes to all of us, I will say to myself: "No! — My whole life depends on my not taking that compulsive bite and no emotion I have can make me give into eating. Besides, I have promised God I won't overeat. I know, He doesn't want me to and I won't break my promise to God. I've given up my right to overeat sweets and starches so it's not my decision any longer."

We can only judge ourselves by our results. Are we losing weight? In times of temptation do we call someone, write a letter, or get a substitute for overeating? If we seek God's help He shall give it.

Have I made this choice once and for all, so that there's no going back?

PRAYER: *I pray that while I'm abstaining from overeating I can see God's purpose for me in life. I pray that I can gently accept what He is trying to teach me.*

* * *

Everyone that has had to diet most of his life knows through bitter experience that he can't eat carbohydrates in small amounts. I seem to crave large amounts of them at stress times. This causes all my problems to become worse, not better. Because after I gain from overeating them I hate myself more and more. Now that I found a way out (to give them up entirely) I will hang onto that idea more and more. I must give them up entirely until I have reached my goal, and I need God's help because I am weak and cannot do it myself.

I know a new life will come for me with proper eating; that when I can control my eating my difficulties won't seem so big. I must trust that it is God's will for me not to overeat.

Am I really ready to give them up?

PRAYER: *I pray that I may welcome difficulties without excess food. I pray that they may test my strength and build my character.*

* * *

When we are overeating most of us have no real faith in anything. We may have said we believe in God, but we didn't act as though we did. We never honestly asked God to help us and we never really accepted His help.

Now we have become desperate enough to ask for help and believe it can come. Faith can give us strength to stop overeating. Have I learned to trust in God and have faith?

I will have faith no matter what my life brings. I will be patient even in the midst of trouble. I will not fear the strain of life because I believe that God knows just what I can bear. I will look to the future with confidence.

Will I trust God?

PRAYER: *I pray that I may put the day in God's hands. I pray for faith so that nothing will upset me and my determination to lose weight so much that I turn to food for comfort.*

When we are overeating most of us are full of pride and selfishness. We believed we could handle our own affairs even though we were making a mess of our lives. We were very stubborn and didn't like to take advice. We resented being told what to do. To us humility looked like weakness, but when we became humble and asked for help that humility gave us the power we needed to overcome our excess desire for food. Have I learned that there is power in humility? Am I willing to call someone and ask for help?

I will come to God in faith and He will give me a new way of life. This will alter my whole existence, the words I speak, the influence I have, the things I do. The words, example, and whole being of a person can have a wide influence for good in the world.

Do I have faith in God?

PRAYER: *I pray that I may learn the principles of a good life. I pray that I may meditate upon them and work at them because they are eternal.*

*   *   *

When we were overeating most of us never thought of helping others. We liked to treat others to goodies and rich desserts because it made us feel important. Food became a very important thing in our lives. We thought about it much too often. To stop eating and do something more constructive never occurred to us. But when we began to try giving up snacks and did something helpful for others we found a happiness never experienced before.

Am I helping others?

PRAYER: *I pray for strength that God's will be done. I will use God's unlimited store of strength for my needs. I will seek God's will for me. I will strive for consciousness of God's presence for He is the answer to life's problems. I pray that I may seek God's guidance day by day. I pray that I may improve constantly in all ways of life besides eating.*

*   *   *

The more we overeat the more food means to us. It is a very unnatural way of life. On just three meals a day we have time to think more sensibly. During our compulsive eating days our lives weren't any more difficult than the lives of more normal eaters, but as we became more obese we became more and more disturbed. Do I realize that the past overeating can stop and I can become normal? I will say thank You God for everything, even the seeming trials and worries. Because sometimes good and better things come out of them. I will strive to be humble and grateful for all of life. There is a purpose for it. My whole attitude of a Higher Power will be one of gratitude. I will be glad for the things I have received and not worry about what I want.

Do I learn from past mistakes?

PRAYER: *I pray for gratitude for the things I receive that I do not deserve. I will try to keep improving myself each day in some way.*

* * *

When we were overeating we were living an unhealthy way of life both physically and mentally. We were punishing our bodies by loading them with food. We didn't eat enough protein and vegetables and ate too many sweets and starches. We couldn't sleep sometimes because we hated ourselves so much or we had indigestion. We knew we were ruining our lives but didn't seem to be able to change. We had an obsession for overeating that was so strong that we couldn't change it. We even wondered if we were mentally ill.

Now that I have help from this book, am I getting better?

PRAYER: *God help me to never despair or have self pity now that I have found a road to recovery. If I should fall and make mistakes in my eating habits or any other phase of my life, let me forgive myself as I already know you do. Help me to keep trying.*

* * *

When we first started eating only three meals a day life seemed strange to us. We had so much extra time. Now we could think about other things besides food. The longer we stayed on just three moderate meals, the more we felt like a normal person. We can accept ourselves as a whole person and have a full satisfying life with other important activities.

Do I believe that three meals a day is the best eating plan for me?

PRAYER: *God keep me strong on my new controlled eating plan. Let me be victorious over temptation to snack like so-called normal people.*

* * *

Three meals a day is a good way of life. It helps us to self-discipline if we want to lose weight and keep it off. Another discipline I need is to call another overeater at times of temptation. I need a quiet time each day to get a better perspective of my life. I need some kind of exercise beside my usual work.

Have I acquired self-discipline in all these phases?

PRAYER: *God help me to relax and not get tense so I won't feel the need for extra food. Put fears out of my mind because I know things will work out for the best. I realize now that some things are blessings in disguise. Give me strength for each new day.*

*   *   *

I am not only losing weight; I am building a new way of life for myself and others about me. Just to stop overeating is not enough. Even when I reach my goal I realize I have to keep working at the program of self-improvement. In our bingeing days we kept going downhill, but now we can get better and better.

Am I getting better?

PRAYER: *God, I will obey Your will in all things I do. I will strive daily to have wonderful experiences in the little things that are important to my well being. I will try to be friendly to all I meet, so others will be glad they know me.*

*   *   *

It doesn't do much good to go on a diet off and on. This only frustrates us because it won't help much in the long run. Sooner or later we have to come to a sensible way of eating and stick to it. Building a new way of life is necessary for complete control.

Am I spending enough time and energy to obtain this new way of life?

PRAYER: *God help me to succeed in all that is good for me. I will get strength from you to change my wrong attitudes about life. When I start to worry or get impatient, I ask you to remind me in some way how I can be better.*

*   *   *

This new life cannot change overnight. We must take change slowly, a little at a time. Every day and in every way we are getting better and better. Our subconscious minds have to be re-educated. We have to learn to think differently. We have to get used to right thinking about food. Anyone who has tried dieting knows that old compulsive habits can come back on us when we least expect them. Building a new life is a slow process, but it can be done if we really follow the steps in this book.

Am I building a new life for myself?

PRAYER: *God help me to have enough faith so that I can control my eating. Let me work to help myself. Let my attitude about food, people, and You be of a positive nature only.*

* * *

On the plan of only three meals a day we can plan our lives around honesty, unselfishness, faith in God, and love of our fellow men. We'll never reach our complete goals in life, but the adventure of changing is so much better than the frustrations of our old eating life that there is no comparison. We read this book to lose weight, but if we stay with this book's ideas long enough, it can open up a new wonderful life for us. We can become honest in other areas as well. We look back on the old things we used to do and say that they were dishonest and realize how much unhappiness they caused.

Have I changed my thinking and become honest?

PRAYER: *God, I know You can answer my needs so please help me to be open-minded to Your spirit. Help me to see the plans for my life that You want for me. I pray that I may understand my real needs and wants.*

* * *

We are all through with lying about how much food we eat and about other things that we tried to tell others which we knew weren't true. Now we're trying to live decent, honest, unselfish lives; we're really alive for the first time. Life has a new meaning for us, so that we can be of some use in the world. We're on the right track. We can look the world in the face and be sociable instead of staying home and being ashamed of ourselves. Am I convinced that no matter how much I used to enjoy food, that my life is much more enjoyable now?

PRAYER: *Let me set my deepest thoughts on a spiritual life. Let me think on good thoughts so I can be good.*

* * *

In order to accept a change in our lives we have to think things out. We can be transformed by renewing our minds. We have to get our thinking straight. We must get a new way of looking at carbohydrates. To us they are very harmful. To our bodies they do us damage by making us gain weight. Other people can eat them and not gain, but we cannot control our desires for them so we must give them up entirely. Only when we reach our desired weight goal can we eat small amounts of them.

Am I giving them up?

PRAYER: *God, keep me strong in my desire to lose weight. Let me be confident in my capacity to abstain from overeating. I pray that I may be calm and let nothing upset me. I pray that I may not let foods control me and choke out my new spiritual growth.*

*   *   *

In the beginning you want to lose, but you're helpless, so you turn to a Power greater than yourself and by trusting in that Power you get strength to stop overeating. From then on you want to keep strong, so you must let this Power change your mind. Later, you will really enjoy the simple good foods that God has given to us. You begin to realize that most of the fattening foods are man-made. About the only natural vegetables that are fattening are potatoes, corn, peas and lentils; also beans and rice. They are not too fattening if taken in moderation, but be sure you're not compulsive on any of them before putting them in your food plan.

Am I giving up improper foods?

PRAYER: *God help me re-educate my mind about what kinds of food are best for me. Let me learn to enjoy the foods that you have planned for my healthy body.*

*   *   *

A compulsive eater is a person whose life is controlled by his obsession for food. He hasn't been able to control his eating. He is always making the same mistakes and suffering from weight gain. Over and over he tries to eat foods like a normal person. He thinks that some day he will be able to take a small dessert or a "goodie" without wanting more. He won't swallow his pride and admit he is different from ordinary eaters. He won't face the fact that he must spend the rest of his life without sweets and starches. He can't visualize himself not enjoying them.

Am I on the road to recovery or am I still going to try to be a normal eater?

PRAYER: *God, give me the power to give up the foods that I have no control over. Let me be sensible about it and accept it gladly. I will need You to help me to live without them. You can give me the strength to say "No thank you" to my friends that tempt me.*

A compulsive eater refuses to be really honest with himself or with other people. He sometimes sneaks food and eats alone in private, but he is miserable doing it. He keeps making the same mistakes. He's using food to anesthetize his body and mind so he won't have to face things as they really are. He's too sensitive and too easily hurt. He refuses to try to be unselfish. He refuses to diet. No matter how much unhappiness his eating causes him, he refuses to give it up.

Have I changed my sneaky ways of overeating?

PRAYER: *God, I know that Your powers are limitless and they can flow through me. Let me submit my faults to you. Let me take one step at a time to improve. Let me feel the freedom when I am doing Your will.*

* * *

This book should help us to take a long view of eating instead of a short view. When we were overeating we thought more about pleasure or release that a bite would give us than we did about the consequences of weight gains as a result of taking that first bite of fattening foods. Candy and cookies and other so-called "goodies" looked so good to us. We saw them in fancy packages and couldn't resist buying them. Of course we used the excuse that we had to have them for the family, but we knew that we were going to get more than our share. We always picked the kinds that were our favorite. They looked so delicious. Have I learned that what is in these fancy packages are just plain harmful to me? For normal eaters they are O.K. But for me they are just ruinous. My body and mind can't take them.

Have I learned?

PRAYER: *Teach me O God, to believe that refined carbohydrates are harmful to me. Let me resist their temptation and the thought of indulging in a bite which could mean a "binge." I pray that I may grow spiritually in my struggle for control of my desire to overeat.*

* * *

The bakeries and candy stores used to look so inviting to us. But we don't stop anymore because if we go in there we will end up gaining weight from anything we might buy.

Do I avoid stores that sell only fattening foods?

PRAYER: *I pray that I may avoid being tempted to go to places where refined carbohydrates are sold exclusively. I pray that You will help me to put into my body only the foods which will keep me healthy.*

* * *

If we are going to stay slim, we have to want something else more than we want to overeat. When we first started losing weight, we couldn't imagine wanting anything else more than food. We had to stop overeating by faith, so that some day we would want something else more than food. Now we really can enjoy more important things in life. We learn how nice it is to buy well-fitting clothes, how comfortable it is to sit in a chair, or how good it feels to walk down the street with pride for the new figure we acquired.

Do I have all these wonderful feelings?

PRAYER: *Help me to continue on my search for the real needs of my body, mind and spirit. Grant me courage to show others the way to stay slim and happy.*

* * *

When we look back on the money we spent on regular doctors, weight doctors, pills and reducing machines, we wonder why we thought they would help. Now we know that only our own determination and God are necessary for recovery from our weight problem and any other problem which is of an emotional source. We are glad we are out of that rat race of staying constantly on special diets. All we have to do is eat proper foods in the right amount and we will stay thin. We won't go back to our compulsion for certain foods again.

Have I experienced serenity in my eating habits?

PRAYER: *God, You can help me to abstain from overeating the rest of my life so that I don't ever have to be fat again. Help me to remember that I cannot do this alone.*

* * *

Now that we have stopped overeating, we can be glad when morning comes. We can get out of bed and be grateful to God that we feel well and happy instead of sick of ourselves and disgusted. Serenity and happiness have become much more important to us than the anticipation of eating. Foods such as sweets lift us up only for a short time when we are indulging in them, but they are our enemies in the end. Of course certain foods taste good. We might as well admit it. We can look back on a lot of good times eating, but the time comes for all of us compulsive people to cease having fun by eating fattening foods.

Have I learned to eat to live instead of eating for enjoyment?

PRAYER: *God help me rely on You for guidance and trust in You to keep me from eating foolishly again. I know that some day I will no longer crave to overeat.*

* * *

In the past, we kept right on eating in spite of all the weight we gained. We were foolish to keep trying to find satisfaction in food. We know a lot of people who enjoy overeating, but we realize they too are not as happy doing it as they pretend to be. We have found out that we were not the only odd people who craved sweets and starches. After realizing this we could accept ourselves better.

Have I learned to admit that overeating is no longer a pleasure for me, and gives me no fun but lots of trouble?

PRAYER: *No one can be tempted to indulge in too much food if He is in tune with You, God. You can save me from doing wrong. Help me keep from turning to food when I become emotionally upset.*

* * *

At weddings or parties where we are confronted with foods we shouldn't eat, we should enjoy the occasion without eating. Very few people care if we eat or not, and they can see by our bodies that we don't need the extra food. If they try to get us to eat, they are not our friends, but friendly enemies. If we are tempted just to have a good time by helping make the hostess happy, we usually go home very disgusted with ourselves for giving in to the temptation. We are beginning to think less about the pleasure of the moment and more about the consequences.

Has eating at special occasions become less of a temptation to me lately?

PRAYER: *Help me, O God, to continue my search for abstinence from compulsive overeating. Strengthen me with Your spirit. Guide me in the right pathways to a new understanding of my real needs.*

* * *

When morning comes and I wake up remembering my terrible compulsion for foods the night before, I feel like crawling back into bed to escape the scales. I know I probably have gained weight. I can't be honest with myself in my eating. I know I need a Higher Power, but I am so stubborn. Maybe I just want to be miserable and fat.

Can I be honest with myself?

PRAYER: *God, help me to realize that I don't have to continue in this kind of life. I can let You lift me out of my despair. Please help me!*

*   *   *

There is some desire to overeat either conscious or unconscious, that comes before every binge. As long as we live, we must be on the lookout for such thoughts of how good some fattening foods taste, and guard against them. We must train ourselves so we can be prepared for such thoughts at once and reject them. The slip comes when we allow such thoughts to remain in our minds, even before we actually go through the motions of eating.

How well have I trained my mind to leave certain foods alone?

PRAYER: *I pray that I may be humble and ask God to keep me from giving in to temptation.*

*   *   *

Why do slips occur? Because we don't accept the fact that we are not able to eat normally. We are compulsive eaters and we must not forget that. We can try to eat like a normal person for a period, but sooner or later it leads into a binge.

Can I be the exception to this and try to eat like a normal person?

PRAYER: *God, help me to be loyal to myself and not give in to overeating. God, be present in my personality. I know You will help me if I only ask You. My prayers can be answered. I pray that my life can be close to You and to my fellow man.*

*   *   *

In spite of all we do there will probably be a slip now and then. We forget or refuse to call on a Higher Power for help. We seem to deliberately make ourselves forget God just so we can give in and eat. Those who have given in to eating binges say they are no fun; they take all the pleasure out of eating. They knew they were doing the wrong thing. The old mental and emotional conflict was back in full force. They were disgusted with themselves.

Am I convinced that I can never enjoy overeating again?

PRAYER: *God help me to give to others who are having trouble the sympathy, love, and time so they too can be helped. Let me*

*give others confidence as I have been given it by You. I pray
that I may have the right answers for those who are confused.*

* * *

If we overeaters allow ourselves to dwell on how good some
food tastes, for any length of time, we are in danger of having a slip
or a binge. Therefore, we must dispel such thoughts at once, by refusing their admittance and by immediately putting constructive
thoughts in their place. Remember that refined carbohydrates are
harmful to our bodies. Remember that it is impossible for us to eat
them like normal people. Think of the reasons we are on a diet. It's
because we can't handle these so-called "goodies".

Can I handle them?

PRAYER: *Let me evaluate the things in the world which seem wrong
and try to judge only by those values which seem right for
me. Let me seek no praise from others. I must do this for
myself alone. I must have peace of mind and serenity.*

* * *

The way for true and lasting success is to find a faith which
can help us to stay on our diet. Until we surrender our lives to some
Power greater than ourselves, we can expect to have times of failure.
There is no other way for us. We can lose weight without God's help
but we cannot keep it off without His help. Life is not a search for
happiness. Happiness is a by-product of living the right kind of life,
of doing the right things. Do not search for happiness, search for the
right living and happiness will come. Have I been humble enough
to admit I cannot do this myself?

Do I admit I need God?

PRAYER: *I pray that I may not seek happiness alone, but seek to do
right. I pray that I may not seek pleasure so much as the
things that bring true happiness.*

* * *

Service to others makes the world a good place. Civilization
would cease if each man was always and only for himself. We overeaters have a wonderful opportunity to contribute to the well-being
of the world. We have a common problem. We find a common
answer. We can share with others our problems so as to better understand ourselves. Then we can help others who still suffer.

Do I really want to get well?

PRAYER: *Today I can live in the consciousness of God's contact, holding on to good thoughts and deeds. If at times I face trials in my life, I will remember that God is not forgetting me, but I have probably forgotten Him. I pray that there will be a better day.*

* * *

Christmas Season: Many overeaters will be saying, "This is a good Christmas for me." They will be looking back over past Christmasses and other holidays with fear and trembling. They will be thanking God for their mature thoughts about food and overeating. They will be happy to be able to eat in moderation without that full, bloated feeling. Perhaps God let them have these horrible experiences so they could grow more spiritually.

Is this a happy Holiday for me?

PRAYER: *I pray that I may be thankful for this Christmas season, and thank God that I have control of my eating. I realize that He whose birth we celebrate would not approve of my being a glutton. To be one is not the best way to celebrate this season.*

* * *

As we look back over our eating compulsions we realize that our lives were a mess because we were a mess inside ourselves. The trouble was in us, not in life itself. Life itself was good enough, but we were looking at it the wrong way. We were looking at it emotionally instead of logically. We could not see all the goodness and purpose in the world, because our thinking was dulled by overeating. All we could see was how miserable we were.

Can I now look at a life without large amounts of fattening foods?

PRAYER: *I pray that my fear of overeating will vanish and not get me down. I pray that I may try to place myself today under the protection of Your grace, oh God.*

* * *

Today is the only day I have. I will live it to the best of my ability. I will start out with a quiet time to get a better perspective of my life. I'll get a personal contact with God as I understand Him. Each minute and hour will bring me closer to His purpose for my life. I'll eat right, live right and think right. Then at night I can go to bed and thank Him for all I've done.

Am I grateful for this day I've lived?

PRAYER: *God, help me believe that You can save me from old mistakes. Keep me in the way that I should go. Rescue me from temptation so I can go onward to a disciplined life. Let me depend upon You so that I will not stray.*

* * *

Faith in God can help overeaters to overcome loneliness, fear and anxiety. It can help us to get along better with people. It can make it possible to rise above pain, sorrow, and despondency. It can help us to overcome our compulsions for food.

Have I decided to have a faith in God?

PRAYER: *God, help a miracle to take place in my life. I know it can if I but trust in You. I know I can be changed and am ready right now to go along the right path. My personality can be changed by Your spirit so much that my desires for fattening foods can be gone — they can completely vanish and I can be free of them. Let me expect this miracle in my life.*

* * *

Many of us fight new ideas, such as a spiritual life we've never had. We refuse to rely on any power other than our own. We feel we are being strong and independent, but actually we are weak and helpless. We are asking for trouble when we try to live our lives without God. Anxiety and inferiority always come when we depend on ourselves too much.

Have I ceased to rely on myself too much?

PRAYER: *God, help me to rise above doubt and fear of You. Let me truly believe, and get off the fence. Let me have no more doubts, but belief so I can act and do the best thing for my life. Let me accept Your power which You eagerly give to me, if I only will take it. Let me venture along in this new faith and trust in Your divine guidance.*

* * *

Other overeaters, who have lost weight and kept it off, can look back and see where they were out of control long before they finally admitted it. Every fat person goes through a stage of not admitting they were compulsive overeaters. They thought they just ate the wrong foods, but we know that too much food is also a reason for overweight.

Do I admit that I am a compulsive eater and have no control over sweets and starches?

PRAYER: *God, help me find a good force in my life and cooperate with this force, so that I will choose the right kind of foods and the right amounts, and eat only three meals a day. Let me keep from wanting snacks. Let me bring all my desires and change under Your spirit so I can become successful in my life.*

*   *   *

I used to be sick not only of my body but myself. My emotions were all negative. I hated my life and everyone in it. In spite of all this, I still had my family and a few friends. I guess God's love was with them; that's why they could accept me. I know now that His love is with me too, even when I didn't feel it, because now I can love others and myself. I used to make a fool of myself and even when I tried to control my eating, I failed. I didn't believe carbohydrates were so harmful to me. I loved to eat them so much that I believed they were good for me.

Do I now believe these foods are ruinous for me?

PRAYER: *Let me painfully see myself, Oh God, as I really am; a fat person who has no control over food. Let me be humble enough to admit it to you, to myself and someone else, so I can get release. Someday I know that You can help me find the answers to my dilemma. I pray that I may test myself and trust that You will get me through each meal, each hour and each day.*

*   *   *

Many of us have studied health books, diets, and other things for overweight. In every case the relief was only temporary. We excused ourselves by saying we had gland trouble or water retention, when we knew deep down in, it was just too much food. We were not able to become honest with ourselves or others. Overeating got to be such a habit that it was becoming an illness and obsession. We became sick of our bodies and ourselves and felt we were destroying our minds and bodies.

Do I realize that overeating is an illness?

PRAYER: *Let me have faith that this disease of compulsive overeating can be cured. Let me believe I can help myself change because You are with me. Your spirit and love can help me change. I will be well.*

Until we read this book we believed we were like other people, that we could eat socially and have an occasional snack. We tried time and time again to lose weight but our social eating and snacking prevented us from doing so. People got disgusted at our size. We wanted to stop eating too much but couldn't. Now we realize that this is because we are compulsive overeaters. We are not normal eaters and may never be. What a shock to face the truth! The truth hurts but it can also set us free. Free to eat right, live right and lose weight.

Am I willing to face my compulsive self and get hold of my emotions?

PRAYER: *God, when things upset me, never let me turn again to food. Keep me on my diet because that is my assurance of right thinking. It looks rough to me at times, to give up sweets and starches, but now I know that is my only answer. Let me seek Your direction so You can steer me on the straight course of action.*

* * *

A compulsive fat person is unable to or unwilling to live in the present because he lives in constant fear of the future and remorse of the past. The only real hope for him is to face the present as he now is with all his shortcomings. Now is the only day we have, because the past is gone and the future is very uncertain. We can have today only.

Am I living today as I want to live it?

PRAYER: *God, help me forget the terrible past. Let me change the things I can, but let me forget the past that I can't change. I must not carry burdens of my past with me anymore. I am not the same person I used to be. Let me go on in a new faith.*

* * *

I must continue to strive for improvement. Losing weight is not enough. I must improve my mind and spirit. There can be no stopping or resting place, but I must keep going upward. I must realize that my goals in life will never be completely reached. If they were there would be no more purpose for my living. Life keeps me going to better and newer heights.

Am I constantly improving?

PRAYER: *God let this life be a preparation for the future. Show me Your plan for my future so I can try to make it come true.*

Let me prepare myself for better things by doing today the best that I can. Let me trust in You for my every good desire.

* * *

I have proven to myself that life is basically an inner attitude. When I try to remember what bothered me a week ago I find it difficult to remember. Why should I fret about the problems I have today? My attitude can change my situation. If I can't change it then I can leave it in God's hands and I know that it will turn out all right, providing I am doing all I can to do the right thing. My changed mental attitude toward my daily problems can relieve me of their burden and I can then face them without fear.

PRAYER: *God, I cannot see the future so let me stop worrying about it. Let me trust in You so I won't have to think about what is going to happen. May I be confident that You will send only the best for me. Let me leave my future to You. Keep me on the right path so I can be confident that my future will be good.*

* * *

If we take each trouble as it comes and fit ourselves to it we can maintain our calmness and rise above it. This is a priceless asset which we all should strive toward. Even if we are forced to go through life with a burden put upon us we can succeed because we have accepted life. It's no good to fight what is. So be it.

Have I learned to accept the bad with the good?

PRAYER: *Let me be a blessing to others. Let me show by my love for You, this love to others. Let me pass on each blessing I get to someone else. I pray that it will flow into the lives of others.*

* * *

Sometimes we have been overeating because of past wrongs, and if we face them intelligently and talk about them and forgive ourselves, all our eating problems could vanish. We know God has forgiven us long ago. We still are trying to punish ourselves by overeating. How long do we intend to do this? Overeating is a disease because our minds are diseased with negative thoughts. We must get well in our thinking so our bodies can lose weight.

Have I fully accepted my past and forgiven others and myself?

PRAYER: *God, help me find proper time for my meditation, reading, and exercise. I know You want me to do all of these things because they will help my life in many ways. My future happiness depends on my self-discipline. Lead me to new insights in the best ways to achieve this new life.*

* * *

One of the most encouraging facts is that our weaknesses can become our greatest assets. If we face our weaknesses and admit them, examine the reasons for them, then we can find out how to rise above them. No weakness such as overeating can be changed unless it is first faced and admitted.

Am I changing my weakness into a more constructive life?

PRAYER: *God, I have the desire to worship You, but I feel so far away. Get hold of me and let Your spirit come into my life. You really are in me and I know it, so please let me feel it now. Today. Just as I am. Let me experience Your Power in my life.*

* * *

Refined carbohydrates are our weakness. The beginning of our overeating started because of our unstable emotions. We just turned to these fattening foods for comfort. They acted like a sedative for our nerves. We suffer from mental conflicts and try to escape by eating. We try to push away what is happening in our lives. Food is no way for us to solve our problems. It really doesn't help, in fact it makes us worse. We get more frustrated each time we overeat.

Have I learned that food will not cure my problems?

PRAYER: *God, help me to get rid of resentments that interfere with my love for You and myself. Let no one or my opinion of anyone interfere with my life because I need a clear guidance from You to go forward, not backward. Give me the right attitude toward others, even if they do hurt me.*

* * *

Intelligent faith in God gives us the stability to control our emotions. It gives us a capacity and a new balanced perspective. We can look upward and around and away from our old eating habits to the real things that matter in life. Our problems begin to solve themselves without our even trying. We stop criticizing others and learn to like everyone.

Have I been changed enough to see a new me?

PRAYER: *God help me to have a spiritual life so that I can have a serene mind. Let me keep calm in this troubled world. Keep my faith in You ever present no matter what happens.*

We have this choice every day of our lives. We can overeat, get fat, and be miserable. Or we can abstain, lose weight, and be happy. It is our decision; no one else's. No one can do it for us. Not our parents, our spouses, our children, our friends, our doctors, or any one but us. God alone can help us if we let Him. The choice is ours each day of our lives.

Have I made a good choice today?

PRAYER: *God help me to choose to live a spiritual life so that my physical life can be controlled. Let me seek good for myself. Let me grow in wisdom and power to overcome my obsession to eat.*

*   *   *

Have I learned that refined sweets and starches are my worst enemy? I used to think of them as delicious and tasty but they were the cause of my weight gain, so I now call them harmful in order to give them up willingly. When I look at the fat on my body I know what damage they did. I can't take one "goodie" so I must give them up entirely, at least until I reach my goal. I know what would happen if I went back to my old desire for something sweet. My troubles would begin all over again.

Is it still important for me to abstain from snacking and man-made carbohydrates?

PRAYER: *God, it is not my circumstances that need altering much, but it is myself. Help me to change my attitude and I'm sure my conditions in life will change. God help me strive to be all You want me to be. Let my conscience be my guide. Let me not look back but forward. Let me take each problem in prayer so You can give me the right answer. Let me do today what I can do.*

*   *   *

We overeaters have to believe in a Power greater than ourselves. Yes, we must believe in God. Not to believe sends us to atheism and that alone sends us to eating. It is hard for us to believe that this world started with nothing spiritual and goes nowhere. That's practically impossible to believe. Even if we don't feel God's presence, we want to believe He's here waiting for us to believe.

Have I decided there is a God to help me?

PRAYER: *Thank you O God, for the gift of peace which can never be taken away from me. You can give it to me in the midst of all my trials and tribulations. I will value my spiritual life more than my physical world. Give me an inner peace that lasts.*

* * *

Since losing weight and giving up compulsive eating, I have such a better physical feeling. No more headaches, backaches, leg aches, stomach aches or other aches. Many of my physical pains have vanished because my body is more healthy. I'm not so nervous, and I don't have to take pills for sleeping or pep or any other neurotic reason. I can now look my family and others in the face and be proud of myself. I remember that my Higher Power is constantly with me, guiding me away from any tempting fattening foods. Do I miss these foods that I am giving up?

PRAYER: *God show me the spark of your spirit which is in us all. Let me continue to live as You want me to and not as my will wants. Let me be transformed from a physical being to a spiritual one.*

* * *

Overeating is a progressive illness. We go through the three stages: Social eating, too much at meal time, then sneak eating. We sometimes get up in the middle of the night and eat. We keep getting fatter and fatter. We eventually get so bad and so compulsive that we begin to wonder if we are sane. Sometimes we wish we had to go to a hospital to "withdraw" from food. Or we wish we could be locked up and handed three small meals a day. We get on this eating-eating-eating- and don't know how to stop. Do I know that God is the only one who can help me?

PRAYER: *Let me know a new life and grow in grace and beauty. Let me reach forward and upward to Your spirit. Let my whole personality change with Your loving spirit. Let me be honest, and unselfish. I need to be changed completely, Oh God, so I trust in You to help me with this task which is too big for me. We can do it together, one day at a time, one problem at a time.*

* * *

Once a person is "hooked" on refined carbohydrates he almost always remains that way. He never gets better, but gets worse. Even if he takes off weight by diet, and if he doesn't have faith in a Higher Power, he probably sooner or later will gain all of it back plus some more. He trusted in his doctor or himself or someone else too much. No person alone can help a compulsive overeater. God is the only one. May we find Him now.

Will I be humble enough to turn to God for help?

PRAYER: *God, my body is here on earth for one purpose — to do your will. Let me choose the spiritual life instead of the life that suits my desires. May I accept this belief so I can mold my character best suited for me. My soul is trained by the good I do and what I accomplish. I pray that I may realize God's purpose for my life.*

* * *

When we reached the bottom we finally had to climb up. We hated ourselves and were sick of our way of living and eating. Life had become impossible for us. We either had to end it all or do something, so we found God. He has helped us accept our miserable selves and climb out of the fat body into a spiritual being of trimness and health.

Am I on the road to recovery?

PRAYER: *Faith is not seeing, but believing I can do something. I must unite my purpose in life with God's purpose for me. I must get my mind to thinking with God's will. This results in a whole feeling of oneness with Him. I can be in harmony with others. Only temptations come when I am not in harmony with You, Oh God.*

* * *

It helps us to share with other overeaters the pitiful life we used to live. When they see our trim bodies it will give them courage to pull out of their fat ones and reach for a new strength which will guide and take them into a trim body also. We feel much better now and we can admit our past overeating. We can continue seeking to help others. No one understands a compulsive overeater more than another overeater.

Am I sharing my success with others?

PRAYER: *God, give me strength to stay on the right course of action and the assurance of Your love. I need belief in You and myself to overcome temptations, so I will keep my faith strong. I will trust in Your spirit each day and hour to guide me as I live them.*

* * *

One of the finest things a person who has lost weight can do is to share his experiences with other compulsive overeaters. Sharing is a wonderful thing because the more you share, the more you have. In our old eating days we didn't like to share. We used to keep food and all other things for ourselves. Partly because we were just selfish, or because we were ashamed of how much we ate and didn't want to share. When we gave up snacking we learned to share ourselves with others. Our time wasn't taken up eating.

Am I sharing my new life with others?

PRAYER: *God, mold my character in my daily disciplined life. May I be obedient to Your voice and take the right path. May I trust in You but depend on myself to act as I should. I pray if I fail I will keep trying.*

*   *   *

Many of us who have reached our goal found out the best way to lose weight regularly was to keep an honesty food chart. We were so used to being dishonest with ourselves that we needed the discipline of making a list of all food before we ate it. This helps because we see what we consume and can tell if these foods will help us lose. Some of us even went so far as counting calories and carbohydrate grams. All of these disciplined ideas of the chart are good. Now we can keep a mental chart and be honest all the time with ourselves, because we have Faith in our Higher Power. We can relax and know we won't gain weight as long as we keep on a protein, vegetable, and some fruits, diet.

Am I willing to keep an honesty food chart?

PRAYER: *God help me this day to begin my disciplined life of eating the right things and proper amounts of them. I have been so dishonest with myself, but I know I can count on You to help me be honest in the future. Guide and bless my endeavor to be an honest person in all of my actions and words.*

*   *   *

Some of us overweight persons hated to get on the scales. We tried to fool ourselves. We thought if we didn't get on the scales that we wouldn't gain. We couldn't face the larger numbers of weight, so we just stayed off the scales. Some of us wouldn't even own scales. We would actually tremble when the doctor asked us to get on one to weigh. We couldn't face the poundage. Now that we have been depending on God's guidance we can weigh once a week and feel sure we are losing. We can face the scales because it's numbers are going down.

Am I weighing regularly and losing weight?

PRAYER: *Dear God, bless me this day as I strive to lose weight. Let the scales be only an instrument, and You my Higher Power. Give me the self-discipline of regular weekly weighing. Let me be honest in other things in my life too.*

*   *   *

Some of us were so compulsive on eating, that many times we had to have toast with our breakfast. We couldn't picture ourselves eating eggs without two or more pieces of toast. Now we've learned to give it up entirely because we couldn't trust our compulsive personalities to one piece. Now we have learned to enjoy a crisp apple or some other fruit instead. We eat a tablespoon of wheat germ to replace any vitamins we need from bread, and this takes away all excuses that everyone needs bread. At lunch we always had to have sandwiches. It seemed unbearable not to have at least two pieces of bread. Now we have learned to substitute for bread other things more healthful and with fewer calories. We used to be too lazy to fix a proper lunch; that's why we grabbed bread. It was so easy to eat. Now we like ourselves better and take time to cook or fix something more "thinning" than bread.

Have I given up my compulsion for bread?

PRAYER: *My God, I thank you that I can have the bread of life instead of bread which makes me fat. I know bread is unhealthy for me because I crave more of it than I need. Help me overcome these selfish desires.*

*   *   *

Some of us overeaters have turned to alcohol as well as food. We found that it got us into worse trouble. Alcohol is also high in calories and upsets us emotionally because we can't stop drinking any more than we could stop eating. What a mess we had become! We must be careful not to change our eating problem to a drinking one. We must get to the root of our compulsive personalities and relax, so we won't have to crave either food or alcohol to calm our nerves.

Have I given up overeating and alcohol?

PRAYER: *God, take away my desire for alcohol besides excess food, so that I will no longer be compulsive on either. Let me use my mouth for speaking truth and love, instead of for overeating or drinking.*

Some of us used to say, "I can lose weight if I just make up my mind to." This was easier said than done. We tried over and over again, only to fall short of our goal. We were hooked on carbohydrates and our lives had become unmanageable. We learned that our minds were not enough to keep us on a weight-reducing plan. We needed a Higher Power to help us. We turned to God as we understood Him and found lasting success; not only in losing weight, but in our ability to abstain from sweets and starches.

PRAYER: *God, I know I am a failure at losing weight and I need You to help me. I can't do it alone. Give me strength and courage to take Your help and the help of others.*

*   *   *

Now that we are not overeating, we have begun to enjoy the benefits of living. We find time to do our work; find time for friends and families; so we are happier and we even begin to like ourselves. We find release from troubles and worries by looking at them differently. We don't have to eat about anything.
Am I enjoying my abstinence from compulsive eating?

PRAYER: *Dear God, Your Spirit is in me. Let it show more and more in my outward person. Let others see my good qualities and let me inspire them to things I now possess. May my motives be on the highest plane so I can expect to understand myself and others more fully.*

*   *   *

After we abstained and lost weight, we began gradually to get peace of mind. We had a serene feeling which we never thought we could ever possess. This peace of mind is based on a feeling that fundamentally all is well. That does not mean that all is well only on the surface of things. Little things do happen and big things can upset us, but deep down in our hearts we know things will turn out all right because we trust in God.
Have I achieved the peace and serenity I need to continue my program of weight loss?

PRAYER: *Let me keep my feet securely on the good steps ahead. Let me climb up and have security as I go onward, so I will not fear falling. You can give me all the power I need to keep climbing, so I can progress steadily all my life with faith and confidence.*

We overeaters used so little self-control when we ate carbohydrates. We were absolutely selfish. It does us good to give them up entirely. Using self-discipline and denying ourselves sweets and starches was the only way. At first it seemed hard even with God's help, but later on we could practice this discipline in other ways as well. It gave us a firm grip on our whole lives so that we wouldn't have to start wishing we could eat them again. If we think about them we might be tempted, so we put them out of our eaing plan.

Am I practicing self-discipline in many ways?

PRAYER: *Dear God, may I not think of material things so much. Food and money made me rely upon myself, but the spiritual things come from You, and I need Your guidance and love to help me to self-discipline.*

*　　*　　*

It is important to keep in a grateful frame of mind because we are fortunate to find out that there are only a few foods that made us overweight. We can give them up and eat plenty of other more healthful ones. We don't have to starve to lose weight. In the old days people used to look down on fat people or feel sorry for them, but now, everyone knows it's just overeating that makes us fat. We can't kid ourselves or others any longer. We are there for all the world to see. We can't hide our size. Am I grateful I found a way to lose pounds?

Am I willing to stop sneaking food?

PRAYER: *God, give me grace and power to refrain from the wrong desires, and give me the effort to act right, live right, and be the right person that I want to be. Let me choose the best path for my life and bless my directions.*

*　　*　　*

I must not brag about my weight loss or new eating plan because I might slip, and then where will I be? I must give God the credit and thank Him for saving me from the mess I was in. I must build myself up in spiritual ways so that I don't have to show off to others. People can see my success for themselves. I don't have to tell them. One bite leads to another so I'm going to stay away from all man-made sweets and starches.

PRAYER: *God, You can help me with this long journey of weight reduction. I cannot do it alone and admit it. I get weary of carrying this burden of fat around with me each day. May*

I be willing to let it fall off my body. There is only one sure way of success in weight loss and that is a dependence on You, Oh God.

*   *   *

Sometimes we fat people try to act funny or happy, when we really are crying inside. We don't really feel inside the way we act outwardly. We don't like ourselves or feel worthy of even being alive. We pretend to be happy so as to cover up our true feelings. We don't binge like others, we just eat one meal a day; all day long! It doesn't seem like much because we never get really full, but we keep gaining. We refuse to face the scales each week, sometimes even for months. That is why we got so fat. We weren't able to get honest with ourselves. We kept trying to cover up by pretending to be happy. Am I ready to get honest with myself and others?

Am I ready to stay on just three moderate meals instead of one meal all day long?

PRAYER: *God, I am in need of a greater power to help me force this old self to a new life. Help me, I pray, to stop pretending and be my real self. Let me believe in Your power because I have none. I need You, God, please help me rise above my desires for food.*

*   *   *

Faith in God can help overeaters to overcome loneliness, fear and anxiety. It can help us to get along better with people. It can make it possible for us to rise above pain, sorrow and despondency. It can help us to overcome our compulsions for food.

Have I decided to have faith in God?

PRAYER: *God, help a miracle to take place in my life. I know it can if I but trust in You. I know I can be changed and am ready right now to go along the right path. My personality can be changed so much by Your spirit, that my desires for fattening foods can be gone; they can vanish and I can be free. Let me expect this miracle in my life.*

*   *   *

Many of us fight new ideas like a spiritual life which we never had. We refuse to rely on any Power other than ourselves. We feel we are being strong and independent, but actually we are weak and helpless. We are asking for trouble when we try to live our lives without God. Anxiety and inferiority always come when we depend on ourselves too much.

Have I ceased to rely in myself too much?

PRAYER: *God, help me to rise above doubt and fear of You. Let me truly believe and get off the fence. Let me have no more doubts but belief so I can act and do the best things for me. Let me accept Your Power which You eagerly give to me if only I will take it. Let me venture along in this new faith and trust in You to help me.*

*   *   *

Many overeaters thought we were "ready to have God remove all our defects of character." This is the 6th step for recovery from compulsive overeating. But we decided that we had to be resentful or angry just one more time. We couldn't give up this desire to "get even" with someone, because we had been hurt. When we really turn our wills over to God we won't have to punish others for what they did to us. We can let God be the judge of them. Our defects are so strong that we must be on constant guard to overcome them and improve. It is a long battle, but when we keep trying we can succeed.

Have I decided to give up my old hurts and resentments?

PRAYER: *Let me live my life, O God, daily in peace and harmony with myself so I will not have to blame others for my troubles. I need Your love and assurance to guide me in the right journey of life.*

*   *   *

Some of us fought the 11th step, "sought through prayer and meditation to improve our contact with God." We thought we could diet and lose weight without a Higher Power, but we always lost our "will power" and realized we needed God. If we believe we have His Spirit within us it is easier to feel His presence in our lives. It is so good to read and meditate because we want to and not because it is a duty.

Am I reading and meditating so I can get serenity?

PRAYER: *God, forgive me for past wrongdoings, of being selfish and not sharing my life with You. Teach me to depend entirely on You for all my needs instead of turning to food for comfort. This peace I get from not overeating will let me get a better perspective of my life.*

Many of us fear taking the moral inventory because we had some unhappy experiences with ourselves and others in the past. The 4th step, "Make a searching and fearless moral inventory of ourselves," is one that we overeaters keep putting off. But if we do go back and admit our past wrongs we can get a new release and begin to feel just great. We must decide to take this step not because we have to, but because we want to stop overeating and feeling guilty. Our compulsive obsessions are caused partly from our guilt feelings.

Do I want to take my moral inventory?

PRAYER: *Help me to rise above old hurts and past wrongs. Today is the only day I have and yesterday is gone. Let me live this day in peace and harmony with everyone near me.*

*   *   *

One of the best things about losing weight and depending on God is the peace of mind and serenity it can bring us. In our overeating days, we had no peace of mind or serenity. We had the exact opposite feeling; a kind of turmoil, and that "quiet desperation" that we hated. The frustration of our overeating days was caused partly because we were so fat and physically unfit. We couldn't play, or run, or walk well. But we also became frustrated by our mental sufferings; the loneliness, feelings of inferiority, and the remorse of every "binge." We didn't feel worthy of being a member of our own family.

Have I achieved more acceptance, love and peace?

PRAYER: *Let my dealings and relationships with others show my love and concern for them. I'm so glad You can keep me from temptation and failure. You can protect me all day long if I but trust, and I will, O God! I shall not doubt that better things are ahead for me.*

*   *   *

We overeaters need a program which comes from our use of medicine, psychiatry and religion. We can take from these sources what we need and combine them into a program of life, best suited for us overeaters. Our minds need all three of these things to help us recover from our compulsions. The results have been amazing for some we have seen. Even miraculous changes have taken place in some lives. Some who were over 200 pounds are now a size 12 in one year, and have kept it off. It is knowledge and practice of these three things that brings lasting success.

Do I try to study these three outlets in my life?

PRAYER: *God, help me strive for a complete oneness in my life. Let my purpose in life be more meaningful and satisfactory. I will get good results if I am in harmony with You and all others.*

*   *   *

We must be careful not to show intolerance to normal eaters. We must abstain from refined carbohydrates, but this does not mean others should or must. This attitude of resentments to others who do not gain weight, only makes us unhappy and isn't helpful to anyone. Moderate portions of these foods are alright for many people, but we compulsive eaters have shown we can't handle them. Our attitude should not be one of bitterness, but acceptance.

Do I have tolerance for those who can eat refined carbohydrates?

PRAYER: *I pray that I may do the things that make for peace with my fellow man. May I try to keep calm and not be so emotional. Give me an inner strength to act the way I believe.*

*   *   *

There is an old saying, "First things First". We should remember that overeating is our biggest problem. We should not let anyone try to convince us we can eat as others do. We learn to recognize the things in life that upset us emotionally. We must try to live each day in peace and harmony.

Am I keeping on the best eating plan for myself?

PRAYER: *God, help me to keep progressing in this better life, that I may be part of the good in the world. May I be a friend to all I meet and may others be glad that they know me.*

*   *   *

Another old motto is "Live and let live". This means that I can accept the point of view of others even though it is different from mine. I shouldn't be critical of others because it could make me upset and I might want to overeat. Let me never impose my will on another person.

Am I willing to live and let live?

PRAYER: *God, help me this day to be openminded to all persons and to what they say or do. Let me be openminded to changing myself in my thoughts and actions.*

We must be willing to make up to all people we hurt so that we can repair past damage. Most people will accept our sincere desire to get ourselves cleared up from past mistakes and blunders. Even our worst enemies will surprise us and forgive.

Have I made an effort to make amends to people I've harmed?

PRAYER: *I pray that I may willingly submit to the necessary discipline to take courage and make amends to others. Let me accept the actions I need to give me a better life.*

* * *

After we have erased all our past wrongs, we must continue to do so as each situation arises in our future daily life. We can grow in understanding and effectiveness and continue to watch for resentment, selfishness, fears, and shortcomings. We cannot rest, and think we are completely well from the past, because we might go back to it. We are never cured from wrong feelings and actions.

Am I checking myself daily?

PRAYER: *God, I pray that I may live each day with others in peace and harmony, expecting no special favors, but giving some extra love to many.*

* * *

Another motto, "Easy does it", is a good one for the overeater to remember. He should take it easy on serving his plate with food. We should be moderate in not only our food intake, but in all our actions, so as not to upset the serenity we are beginning to know. We never used to be able to relax and now we can. We sleep better too. Our faith in God can help us take it easy.

PRAYER: *I pray that I may be at ease with myself and others, not letting little things upset me. Let my serenity be deep and meaningful. Let me be as peaceful as possible.*

* * *

A personal spiritual experience is something that brings about a personality change. By surrendering our lives to God, we change so much that we can actually give up the compulsion to eat. It is real and wonderful, and we now feel mature and able to handle our other affairs. The change is usually gradual, but once in awhile some compulsive eaters who are really desperate get a spiritual awakening over night. They start losing weight steadily and keep it off without any gains.

Do I see myself changing gradually in many areas of my personality and life?

PRAYER: *I pray that I may be conscious of Your support today, O God. Your strength will be available in me as I depend on You this day. Let me never try to be completely dependent on myself, because I know I might fail.*

*   *   *

Am I critical of other overweight people now that I have lost my excess weight? Do I realize that a doubtful or skeptical attitude does not help, but harms another compulsive eater? I must show a loving attitude toward others. We should never say, "He will never lose weight." No one is past the stage of changing. We can all change with the right help and spiritual guidance.

Am I keeping a constructive attitude toward other overweight persons?

PRAYER: *God, give me the knowledge to show my concern for others who still suffer from overweight. Show me the right way to help others with this problem.*

*   *   *

Do I try to help make an insecure person feel wanted and relaxed? Do I try to be friends with a "loner?" Am I trying to be nice to others less fortunate? Or do I stay in a special kind of group?

Am I open to all kinds of people as my friends?

PRAYER: *God, help me show friendship to all who are lonely or afraid.*

*   *   *

Is there someone I should go to see, or write a letter to, or do something for? Is there a job I must do and stop neglecting? Let me not procrastinate the self-disciplined life I need, because this is one assurance of my abstaining from the compulsion to eat.

Do I feel that others depend on my doing my share of work?

PRAYER: *God, help my heart to be right so my life can be right. Let the good powers in me be released and usable.*

*   *   *

Am I over most of my sensitiveness, my feelings getting easily hurt? Am I just plain lazy or selfsatisfied? Is my own comfort more important than doing the things I need to do? Can I face up to self-discipline even if it is hard to do? Am I maturing each day?

Am I willing to give of myself whenever possible to help someone?

PRAYER: *I pray that I may learn to be humble and then I will have self-respect. I pray that I may see the good in myself as well as the bad.*

       *   *   *

Now that I have stopped overeating and lost weight, I am beginning to think straight and understand myself better. I've learned many things that used to be the matter with me and now I've changed and am so much happier. I'll never be unhappy again; I was just sick with a disease called "compulsive overeating", but now I've arrested this disease with God's help and He has given me peace and joy. I am not such an odd or different person — in fact — I'm pretty acceptable to most others.

Am I beginning to understand myself?

PRAYER: *God, Your Spirit is in my heart and I feel Your abiding peace. It is so good to be a whole person.*

       *   *   *

Am I content to face the rest of my life without most sweets and starches? I have made this decision for always, because it is very necessary for me to keep weight off, and look nice for myself and others. Nothing will ever tempt me to overeat those foods again. It isn't worth it. My trim body and my peace of mind mean more to me than any food in the world.

PRAYER: *I pray that I may have an unfailing belief in You, O God, and Your strength will keep me on the right eating plan.*

       *   *   *

I have learned to be honest. What a relief! I don't have to sneak food or hide it in private. No more lies about left over food. My body is slim and healthful for all the world to see and I am proud of it. All the past sneak-eating is gone, thank God, and I am free to be a real person. I'm not perfect, but I'm doing the best I can and am not ashamed of any of my actions.

Have I given up sneak eating and am I honest all the time?

PRAYER: *Continue to bless me, O Lord. This new road to recovery is so wonderful. Let others see the miraculous change in me and be benefited by it.*

I have learned to live one day at a time, and realize that today is the only day I'll ever have. I can live now to the best of my ability. I can do what I want today; I can make it the best day ever. This day has been given to me by God, and I will do something worthwhile in it.

PRAYER: *I pray that I can overcome my selfishness and do something for someone each day. Let me think of ways to make others glad they know me.*

*   *   *

After I got my weight down, other good things began to happen. I had more love for others, I felt physically better, I could walk farther distances without getting tired, and I could even exercise. I was a better person in every way. I could cooperate with others' ideas. Have I changed much?

PRAYER: *Help me to continue reaching for new goals of maturity and health. Let me never be too satisfied with myself, but continue searching for ways to improve.*

*   *   *

My relationships with my family have improved. They are no longer ashamed to be seen with me. Now they like me better, because I like myself better. I am no longer a stranger in my own home. Have I found something better in my household?

PRAYER: *Let my family come first in my thoughts and actions. Let me give them all my love. Let them see Your spirit in me.*

*   *   *

I can do things I never did before — run, dance, jump, and sit more comfortably. Being fat made it hard for me to go places in public without discomfort. Chairs seemed too small. I can go to a movie now without feeling stuffed into the seat. I can work and laugh and sing. I can create things with my hands and give love to others. Am I happy now?

PRAYER: *I'm so grateful God, for my trim body. May I never quit being thankful to You for my success.*

*   *   *

Fears and worry used to be the biggest part of my day. When I overate, I'd fear my gaining weight or of someone finding out what I ate. I was afraid to face the scales the next day. I was a nervous wreck from overeating. I feared failure of everything and was sick of myself. I had wrong attitudes, but now that I have surrendered all these fears and worries to God, I am finally at peace and can lose weight gradually.

Have I put my faith in God in place of my fears and worries?

PRAYER: *Let me show my faith by my actions, O God. Let me change my attitude enough to change my life. Let Your spirit work in me each day.*

* * *

My inferiority complex is going away because I can control my eating. I am not escaping in food. I used to be full of resentments and failure. Now I can lift my head high and smile. I can take my responsibilities as they come.

Have I lost my inferior feeling?

PRAYER: *God, let me drop the past loads of inferior feelings and be myself as I really am. A child of Yours who is worthy of love.*

* * *

I have learned to be less negative and more positive. Now most people like me and I like most people. I began to trust people more. I stopped criticizing others so much. I believe in others and my own capabilities. There is much love and truth and good in the world. Now that I have stopped being so negative, I can really enjoy living.

Am I less negative and more positive?

PRAYER: *God, help me be friendly to all I meet and keep a positive outlook with all my acquaintances.*

* * *

We get so discouraged with our earthly life. Sometimes it seems hardly ever free from problems and doubts. We are troubled with many guilt feelings, which make us turn to food. We sometimes get tired of our jobs in life and don't appreciate anything. We must remember that we can love this earthly life by seeking the good in it. We can smile and be glad about the good things that do happen. We can free ourselves from overeating by accepting life one day at a time. Our dissatisfactions in life will become less as we turn to a Higher Power and lose weight. We must think of ourselves as better than we are, so we can achieve that purpose.

Am I accepting myself and improving or still tearing myself down?

PRAYER: *Loving God, give me life as it is good for me. Thank You for giving me this chance to change. Help me to be unselfish and do Your will.*

We must always be on guard against sweets and starches since they will always be around us. People will always try to tempt us with them, but we can not give in to these desires because losing weight is more important than eating certain foods. The satisfaction of tasting fattening foods does not last as long as the loss of weight when we refrain from eating them. How we deal with temptations shows our wisdom. What looks good often times is not so good.

Have I given up temptations?

PRAYER: *Let me be honest and recognize myself for what I really am. Let me be aware of my weaknesses so that I can improve. Let me avoid the things that will harm my future life. Let me practice self-control so that I can gain complete control.*

*   *   *

Some people who are overweight don't want to believe that they can't handle refined carbohydrates. They keep trying, over and over again, only to fail. Some of us are so stubborn, we don't want to admit we can't eat those foods like other people. We hate or fear this kind of life without "goodies". We feel we are being deprived. If we would only look at the situation honestly, it would be easier. Even a normal eater doesn't need refined carbohydrates to keep healthy. In fact many of them would be better off with more protein, vegetables and fruits.

Am I still trying to eat like a normal eater?

PRAYER: *Let me honestly face the truth about myself and my condition. Let me be willing to let go of "traditional" party-eating since it only makes me unhappy. I can enjoy a social function without stuffing myself with foods that I don't need. Let my reasoning power be strong and unlimited.*

*   *   *

Even if you aren't ready to give up entirely the "binge" foods you crave, at least get started. Do it one meal at a time, one day at a time, and soon you'll be able to abstain from them one week at a time. After one week you will have lost some weight and this will give you courage to abstain for longer periods. Follow the advice in this book as much as you can without fighting it. If you fight it, no success will come. Too much anxiety or thinking about what you are giving up only keeps you from losing faster.

Am I trying to give up "binge" foods willingly?

PRAYER: *Forgive my past mistakes and give me wisdom to keep trying so I will not stop improving. I must have a spiritual time each morning reading and praying to keep me from being careless or half-hearted in my efforts to be healthier and happier.*

* * *

Little do some overweight people realize the harm they are doing their bodies by neglect of regular exercise and proper nutrition. They read to improve their minds and they beautify their faces, but what about the body that holds them all? Give it some care if you want these other things to last. Don't neglect the daily care of the body. Your loyalty and progress should improve each day. Hold on to your original enthusiasm you had when you first read this book. Be patient to endure your daily burdens. Greatness lies in doing the best you can.

Am I doing the best I can to improve my health?

PRAYER: *Let me take each hour of the day and do something important with this precious time. Even if it be work, play, or rest, let it be constructive and wholesome. Let me make an effort to be kind, patient, and unselfish.*

* * *

Put your confidence in God and refuse to worry about anything. Just for today, no matter what happens, make up your mind that you are not going to worry. Take care of today's problems as they come, but don't borrow trouble for tomorrw. We think wrongly when we depend upon ourselves, but if we ask God's love to be with us He gives us a serene mind and we will please ourselves and Him both. Let us be guided by reason and faith.

What have I to fear?

PRAYER: *God of love, You will care for me and keep me safe if I only trust in You. I can have daily peace if I believe in Your abiding love. Let me do my best to remedy whatever difficulties arise. Let me accept the outcome as Your will.*

* * *

When you give in to eating the wrong foods and keep gaining, don't despair. You can use this as a sign of need for God. You are too weak to stay on a diet alone. Admit it, and call on your Higher Power. He is near to help if you only want Him. Stop being so proud. You can't win. But His love can help you win. Give in to God's guidance. Enjoy a happy future.

Am I still fighting God?

PRAYER: God, let me keep fighting my temptations. Let me turn my will and mind on to more important things so I will not become discouraged. Don't let me consider myself a failure when I feel like one. Let me be brave and overcome my faults, so I can win my daily battles. Do I have a tendency to give up too easily?

* * *

God can help me to gradually overcome my desire for too many sweets and starches. I may never be entirely safe from their tempting me. They may always appeal to my weakness and I may not be able to avoid being near them, but God's strength and my determination can keep me from eating them. I can correct and remedy situations as they come.

Do I have a firm determination in my daily life to overcome temptation?

PRAYER: God, let me not run away from life, but fight to conquer all wrongs. Let me be humble, patient and take definite action, so I will be strong against the wrongs in the world. Help me have patience to keep calm in my troubles.

* * *

Good intentions to stay on a diet are not enough. The sincere thought and how much the need are essential to true success. There is no perfect serenity and peace in the world, but I can have the confidence I need to diet if I grow each day in goodness and a firm belief in the right actions to take. I must have patience with myself and others. My fears will be conquered by a stronger faith. When I am ready for it, my consolation will come from God.

Am I ready to have the faith I need?

PRAYER: Let me not be discouraged, but rise above all my faults and turn to Your ways. Help me do my best so I won't worry or be discouraged. Let Your wisdom and peace grow as I have ups and downs in my life. This will help my experiences be easier to bear.

* * *

Sometimes after a "binge", we can look back at it and profit from the mistakes. The distress and trouble it gave us at the time can be a reminder to not indulge again. It can help us lessen our foolish pride by showing God how weak we really are. It can help teach us to depend on God more. We come to know how much we want to please God.

Do I prefer to follow the best kind of diet for me or to let my binge foods tempt me?

PRAYER: *God, let me be loyal to myself and Your will. I realize I am not the only one who has to fight temptations and I know that You are the only one who can help my world to become a better one. Grant me grace to see my faults and correct them.*

* * *

We must never turn our backs on the fact that man-made sweets and starches are our "binge" foods and make us gain weight. We can't handle them. If we keep letting them tempt us we can expect a weight gain sooner or later. We must not take this fact too lightly even after we reach our goal. The only way to be able to handle these foods is to change our complete personalities and that will take time. We took a long time getting into this rut and we must be patient with ourselves in getting out of it.

Are we giving up binge foods completely?

PRAYER: *God, don't depart from me as I need You to guide and help me with my new health venture. I need You to help me get rid of evil thoughts and fears that make me unwhole. Let me be humble and admit my bad thoughts and desires.*

* * *

Some of us are just beginners in this meditation business. It takes time before it will affect our daily lives. We read and pray earnestly in order to feel a contact with God. He may seem far off at first, but as we pray and read each day, He will become more real. We will begin to live a richer and fuller and more meaningful life We will get an inner peace so strong that no kind of food will bother us. Food will become unimportant in our lives.

Do I believe all these things?

PRAYER: *Grant that I may never be so proud and foolish as to refuse good advice. Let me be intelligent about my health and the way I care for my body. Advice from books and others who have had success can give me humility and courage to follow suggestions. They can help me defeat my failures.*

* * *

At the beginning of temptation to eat is when we must watch ourselves. It is the first bite that sets us off on a binge. If we resist that first bite it will be easier to overcome the sweets and starches. First comes a thought of how good it will tast. Then the thought of how much we want it — then it seems too late to stop. Only God can help us do this. We alone are too weak.

Am I seeking God's help for overcoming temptation?

PRAYER: *Let me recognize the wrongs that present themselves in my life and not let them overcome me. Grant me strength to resist them. I know I would have fewer faults today if I turned away from the temptations in the first place.*

*   *   *

None of us are perfect and we might be tempted to go off our diet, but that doesn't mean we have to stay off for any length of time. We can profit by these mistakes and stand up and fight them off the next time, by literally removing ourselves from their presence. Sometimes temptations come any time — in the morning — at noon — in the afternoon — in the evening or even when we can't sleep at night. We can meet them within ourselves if we call on God. He is within us if we are willing to fight for what we know is best for us.

Am I reaching above and past temptations to God?

PRAYER: *God let me do Your will and show me the way to happiness. Let me become better acquainted with You so I can speak, think, and act more like You want me to. Help me to reach the good goals in life.*

*   *   *

Lack of determination is when real temptations come, or from no confidence or belief in a Higher Power. Man must work at the virtues he needs and never abandon his good intentions so he will not be tempted by his own faults and weaknesses. God can give me strength in these times. He can help me when things are not going well. I will not get complete relief until I trust in Him.

Will I get lasting assistance without God's help

PRAYER: *God, forgive me for falling back on my determination to do better. Forgive my half-hearted resolutions, but give me the determination to fight my faults. Even when I fail — let me keep trying. Let me be humble and have a sincere effort to fight my failures.*

*   *   *

Since losing weight and giving up compulsive eating, I have a much better physical feeling. No more headaches, back aches, leg aches, stomach aches, or pain of any kind. All my pains and aches have vanished because my body is more healthy. I'm not so nervous. I can now look my family and others in the face and be proud of myself. I remember that my Higher Power is constantly with me for guidance, if I get tempted to eat sweets or starches.

I don't miss these foods do I?

PRAYER: *God show me the spark of Your spirit which is in us all. Let me continue to live as You will want me to and not as my will. Let me be transformed from a physical being to a spiritual one.*

*   *   *

Some of us are too proud to call someone during the week or even on the week ends. We don't want to humble ourselves and admit what we ate that which we shouldn't have eaten. Now that we have turned to a Higher Power, we can call some other compulsive eater and admit our mistakes because we know that is the best way to get back on our diet. We are weak and need all the help we can get. We use the excuse that people are too busy to talk to us or maybe we are too busy to call someone. Well, we learned from bitter experience that we weren't too busy to grab some fattening snack.

Have I been willing to call someone when I overeat or get upset?

PRAYER: *God, help me to be humble enough, yet brave enough to call someone when I get weak or upset. I know I need You and others to help keep me on the right track. Thank You for the knowledge I have and the joy I can possess when living as You want me to.*

*   *   *

It is so good for me now that I have given up compulsive eating. I gave this problem to God. It must stay in His hands and I refuse to take it back. Food is not so important to me anymore. There are so many intersting things in the world for me to do and share. It is good to be able to refrain from eating between meals. I have so much peace and serenity and no guilt feelings. I can do my work well and keep satisfied with life. I can like myself and others more each day. It is good to be alive.

Have I given my compulsive eating up to God?

PRAYER: *Teach me O God, to do Your will, and not let me depend on myself for decisions. Let me choose the right pathway to follow so I can find true happiness, which can lead me to*

*helping others find it also. Let me have faith and trust in You
one day at a time.*

*   *   *

We cannot get along without prayer and meditation. We need
it for our day ahead. We ask God to direct our thinking and our lives
will be on a higher plane if we start our day right. At night we thank
Him for the past day and ask Him to show us the way tomorrow.
Am I trusting in God for each day's experiences and thoughts?

PRAYER: *I pray that You will help me choose the right way to eat,
live, and work. Let me follow the good paths best suited for
my needs.*

*   *   *

This book is offering something intangible. It is not offering
diets as the means to lose weight. It is offering psychological and
Spiritual growth. It doesn't tell you what kind of diet to stay on, it
only tells you what you had better give up, if you inend to get rid
of compulsive overeating and keep your weight down. Any doctor
will agree that the refined carbohydrates that are mentioned in this
book are not essential to your health. If we need a doctor we go to
one, but if we eat proper foods, exercise regularly, and keep faith in
God and love our fellow man, we won't have to go to a doctor very
often.

Am I working on the Spiritual and emotional side of my life as
much as the physical?

PRAYER: *God, guide me to know a more spiritual life because I've
had very little before that I could use as a real tool to help
me keep from excess food. I know if I believe Your spirit
is in me, I will be able to live each day with self-confidence.*

*   *   *

We must not only make up our minds to quit eating refined
carbohydrates, we must stop bingeing on other foods as well. Our
compulsion and craving has to stop. We must make up our minds to
stop going up and down like a "yo-yo". We must be willing to take
the action necessary to take off excess pounds. We can get confidence
by turning to God, or to someone else who has succeeded. A new dieter
needs encouragement from another person who used to be overweight.
Sharing experiences helps keep both strong. We must learn to re-
educate our minds.

Do I do my best to get and give help to others?

PRAYER: *Let Your spirit flow through my body and mind so that I will come to feel as a worthwhile person. God, I ask You to abide in my life this whole day and let me not falter but keep firm in the steps for recovery.*

*   *   *

When an overeater takes his problem away from food and gives it to a Higher Power, he is released from all pressures of life. He gets a feeling of oneness and is not torn apart wondering what to eat. Shall I eat this fattening food or shall I leave it alone? There is not any doubt when he turns to God for help. He stops trying to make his own decision and lets God handle it.

Am I leaving my weight problem and eating problem to God?

PRAYER: *God, You are my healer and strength. I don't even have to ask You to be with me. You are there already, waiting. All I have to do is to take Your love and care. May I rely on Your strength each day as I need it so much. I am too weak to do it alone. When I feel inadequate in a situation I know You can help me to be adequate so I can take the right action. Help me to always do and think the right things.*

*   *   *

Psychologists are also turning to religion because they realize that just knowing about ourselves is not enough. We need the dynamic faith in a Power outside of ourselves on which we can rely. Books of psychology and psychiatric treatment can help little without the strength that comes from God. Ministers and priests are turning to psychology because faith is an act of the mind and will. Faith must be built largely on our own psychological experiences.

Have I been using both psychology and a religious faith for my daily life?

PRAYER: *God, refill me with Your spirit every day. Let me commune with You and feel Your strength in my daily experiences.*

*   *   *

Some of us get our weight down and unconsciously it goes back up. We don't feel that we deserve success, so we eat back a few pounds. Our subconscious plays a big part in our achieving the goals we have set for ourselves. We must believe that we deserve the fullest and best in life. We should not take second best. We can believe that God wants us to be happy. Just because we've been miserable many times doesn't mean that we have to continue in that old rut.

Am I asking God for success and believing I deserve it?

PRAYER: *God, help me to believe I deserve success.*

*   *   *

This new way of eating only 3 meals with no sweets and starches can't be acquired all at once. We have to work at it slowly. We will have to re-educate our thinking on this effort. We have to keep pushing out of our minds the desires for fattening foods. We have to get used to healthful food thinking instead of how good certain foods taste. It will come back to us occasionally — the desire for the wrong foods, but each time we give them up willingly, the stronger we will become.

Am I really eating to live instead of living to eat?

PRAYER: *I pray daily for faith, for You will give it to me if I only ask. Faith can be the result of my prayers. I pray that I may think and live and feel Your presence in my life enough so I can change for the better. As my faith in myself grows — so will my ability to change grow.*

*   *   *

On a proper disciplined eating plan we can build a life of honesty, unselfishness, faith in God, and love for others. We may never reach our desired goal, but life will be so much better than those old bad habits of overeating. We want to get on a good diet and lose weight, but in order to do this we must change our whole life pattern. We must become honest with not only our eating and ourselves, but with others as well. We can learn to be more cheerful, helpful and thoughtful of others and spend less time thinking about ourselves. We learn to depend entirely on God to guide us. Am I being more honest, less selfish and depending on God more? I believe God knows my every need, even before I ask. I believe He has an answer for my life's problems. I must be open-minded and listen to the new ideas and thoughts He sends me.

Am I willing to change?

PRAYER: *I pray that I may understand that overeating is not the real need for my body, but something greater is calling me to accept help from You, O God.*

EPILOGUE

Now that you have read this book, what have you decided to do about your compulsive eating problem? In this book you have been told how to get complete recovery from this "disease" of the MIND and BODY. You have read the Steps For Recovery which are yours for the taking All you have to do is believe and practice them and you will win the joy of a new spiritual life, emotional maturity and become the slim healthy person you have always wanted to be.

Examples have been given of people who have believed and who have applied these suggestions. You, too, can be successful and obtain the same security and peace in your life. Reading this book is not enough. You must persistently practice each idea and suggestion until you have reached your normal weight and possess a wonderful change in your whole personality.

I wrote this book with a sincere desire to help you lose weight and KEEP IT OFF. It will give me a sense of satisfaction to know that my book has helped you. I have absolute confidence and belief in the 12 Step Recovery plan and the principles and suggestions given in this book. *They will work when worked.* If you cannot make them work alone, then get one or more persons to meet with you weekly and start your own Self-Improvement Club, using your own rules and this book as a GUIDE.

I would like to meet you in person, but in case we never have the chance, remember that we are friends. I pray for all compulsive overeaters and know that they are very real, vital human beings with a possibility of changing. God will be with you — *so believe it and be successful!*

APPENDIX

I wish to acknowledge with gratitude permission from the following publishers and individuals to reprint selections and ideas from their copyrighted works.

The College Press. RADIANT POSSIBILITIES OF MARRIAGE. By Allan A. Hunter.

Zondervan Publishing House. THE ART OF UNDERSTANDING YOURSELF. By Cecil G. Osborne.

Unity School of Christianity. DAILY WORD. By Unity, Lee's Summit, Missouri.

E. Charles Watkins, Associate Clinical Professor of Operative Dentistry of University of California Medical Center, San Francisco, California.

To all the other individuals who wish to remain anonymous.

RECOMMENDED BOOK LIST

*Books with y after price can be purchased through Yokefellows Inc.,
Burlingame, California.*

THE ART OF UNDERSTANDING
   YOURSELF
CECIL OSBORNE
Zondervan Publishing House
Grand Rapids, Michigan
  $4.95 y

*This is wonderful for all unhappy
Christians. Church is not enough.
Insight and frankness into one's
needs for a meaningful life.*

PRAYER CAN CHANGE YOUR
   LIFE
DR. WILLIAM PARKER
Prentice Hall, Inc.
Englewood Cliffs, N.J.
  $4.95 y

*Showing how therapy groups can
help change physical illness into
entire recovery.*

THE POWER OF SEXUAL
   SURRENDER
MARIE N. ROBINSON, M.D.
The New American Library Inc.
P.O. Box 2310, Grand Central Station,
New York, N.Y. 10017
  60¢ y

*Offers hope to husbands and wives
who wish to achieve a mature and
satisfying marriage. Recommended
by ministers and doctors.*

THIS IS PERSONOLOGY
ROBERT L. WHITESIDE
The Personology Press
6600 Geary Blvd., San Francisco
  $4.00

*This book explains how our body
structure affects our personality.*

THE JACK LA LANNE WAY TO
   VIBRANT GOOD HEALTH
JACK LA LANNE
Prentice Hall, Inc.
Englewood Cliffs, N.J.
  $4.95

*How you can be changed physical-
ly and given a program of exercise
and nutrition.*

YOU ARE NOT THE TARGET
LAURA HUXLEY
Fawcett Publishers
Greenwich, Conn.
  60¢ y

*Get your feelings hurt easily? You
are not always the one who was
intended to get hurt. Deals with
mental and physical tensions.*

THE REVOLT OF THE MIDDLE-
AGED MAN
EDMUND BERGLER, M.D.
The University Library
Grosset and Dunlap, New York
$1.65 y

How a woman can understand her middle - aged husband. He goes through a sort of menopause, which is both emotional and physical.

THE SEXUALLY ADEQUATE
FEMALE and THE SEXUALLY
ADEQUATE MALE (two books)
FRANK S. CAPRIO, M.D.
The Citadel Press, New York
Each Book $1.50 y

These books are excellent for any married couple. Tells how to overcome inadequacies.

FEEL LIKE A MILLION
CATHARYN ELWOOD
Pocket Books Inc., New York
75¢

This book explains the harm of refined carbohydrates and chocolate. Fascinating facts about what foods your body needs to feel great.

BEYOND ANXIETY
BISHOP PIKE
Charles Scribner's Sons, New York
$1.25

The Christian's answer to fear, guilt, frustration, and despair.

HOW TO STOP WORRYING AND
START LIVING
DALE CARNEGIE
Pocket Books, New York
35¢

How to break the worry habit. Guiding you into confidence, happiness and peace.

THE MASTER KEY TO RICHES
and THINK AND GROW RICH
NAPOLEON HILL
Fawcett Publications, Greenwich, Conn.
Each Book 75¢

*Personal Achievement for Making Money.
Success through a positive mental attitude.*

PSYCHO-CYBERNETICS
MAXWELL MALTZ, M.D.
Pocket Books, 630 Fifth Ave., N.Y.
$1.00 y

How to help you escape life's dull, monotonous routine — make you feel younger, healthier, and more successful!

LET'S HAVE HEALTHY
CHILDREN and LET'S EAT
RIGHT AND KEEP FIT and LET'S
GET WELL (three books)
ADELE DAVIS
$3.95 each for first two
$4.95 for last one

These are controversial books to doctors and some laymen, but very wonderful and helpful to many.

THE POWER OF POSITIVE
THINKING
Norman Vincent Peale
Prentice-Hall Inc.
Englewood Cliffs, N.J.
$4.95

Suggests techniques and gives examples of how not to be defeated but have peace of mind, improved health, and energy.

ALCOHOLICS ANONYMOUS
A.A. World Services Inc.,
P.O. Box 459, Grand Central Station,
New York 17, N.Y.
$4.50

This book will help overeaters who believe they are like an alcoholic in their compulsion for food. The recovery is the same.

BEYOND OURSELVES
Catherine Marshal
McGraw-Hill Book Co., New York
$2.95 y

This book is excellent for anyone who has had tragedy in his life caused by a physical illness.

MANAGING YOUR MIND
Draines and Thetford
The Macmillan Co., New York
$2.75

This book is good for anyone who feels near a nervous breakdown or one who has been through one. It can help you make your body your friend.

YOUR INNER CHILD OF THE
PAST
Missildine
Simon and Schuster, New York, N.Y.
$5.95 y

This is an excellent way to find out why you got to be a compulsive overeater. A must for all therapy.

FACTS OF LIFE AND LOVE FOR
TEENAGERS
Duvall
Popular Library, New York
35¢

To be given to teenagers when parents find it hard to discuss sex.

GUILT AND GRACE
Tournier
Harper & Row Publishing Co., N.Y.
$3.75 y

Most compulsive overeaters are filled with all kinds of guilt. This book helps get rid of guilt, or helps us handle it. Has insights from the Bible.

HOW TO LIVE 365 DAYS A YEAR
John Schindler, m.d.
Fawcett Publications, Greenwich, Conn.
60¢ y

Case histories of success for many miserable and unhealthy persons. All about controlling emotions.

THE ART OF LOVING
ERICH FROMM
Harper & Row
60¢

How to develop our capacity for love; with maturity, self-knowledge and courage.

THE MARRIAGE ART
EICHENLAUB
60¢

Techniques for the physical side of love.

For Teenagers
WHY BELIEVE IN GOD?
OSBORNE
UNDERSTANDING YOUR
PARENTS
BERTOCCI
Yokefellows Inc., 209 Park Road,
Burlingame, California
Each Book $7.00

Excellent for teenagers in helping them to grow up to be mature adults.

SOBRIETY AND BEYOND
FATHER JOHN DOE
S.M.T. Guild, P.O. Box 1194
Indianapolis, Indiana
$4.50

This is the best book for an over-eater to read because it has the 12 Step Recovery Program to follow. If you relate your overeating to the alcoholic, this book is a must.

RADIANT POSSIBILITIES OF
MARRIAGE
DR. ALLEN A. HUNTER
666 West 8th Street,
Claremont, California 91711
75¢

This is a small but meaningful booklet, because of its frankness on the preparation for a happy married relationship. Good for newlyweds or engaged couples.

PAPERBACKS PLUS, 108 EAST DAVIS, MESQUITE
PAPERBACKS PLUS, 2307 ABRAMS, DALLAS
PAPERBACKS PLUS, 407 LAVACA, AUSTIN

SELECT BUYING GUIDE

(subject to buyer's discretion and change without
notice. EXCLUDES TEXTBOOKS)

Airplanes
Alternative Energy Sources
Antiques & Collectibles
Archaeology & Anthropology
Art & Architecture
Architectural Digest
Beautiful bindings
Boating & sailing
Books about books
Chess & games
Children's picture books, Nancy Drew & Hardy Boys
Classic Literature -- very select titles -- obscure
  titles by well-known authors preferred
Comics
Cookbooks
Crafts
Current bestsellers, TIMES LIST, etc.
Dance & theatre arts
Dictionaries, thesauruses (English & other)
Encyclopaedia Britannica & Worldbook (last 5 years)
Erotica
Feminist Literature
Film & Cinema
Folk art and lore
Foreign language novels & poetry
Gardening & how-to books
Gay literature, fiction & non-fiction
Great Books, complete sets only
Hobbies -- trains, stamps, coins etc.
How-to-do-something books -- wiring, plumbing, etc.
Humor -- Mad, Lampoon, Heavy Metal, Peanuts, Bombeck
Large print titles (not "easy eye" but LARGE type)
Mother Earth News & books from Mother's shelf
Nature guides, identification books
Philosophy -- primary sources & scholarly works
Religion -- scholarly works and references
Science-Fiction
                  . . . and other select volumes

TRADE-IN POLICY
PAPERBACKS PLUS of MESQUITE, DALLAS & AUSTIN
TRADE-IN POLICY

We accept trade-ins for up to 50% of our regular price on USED books, records, etc, excluding science-fiction/fantasy.

This means that with CREDIT from trade-ins, your cost on the average used paperback is only 1/4 of the publisher's price in <u>cash</u>. Without trade-ins, that same book would cost you 1/2 of the publisher's price in cash.

Credit allowed for your trade-ins is generally half to one third of what we hope to resell your books for, depending upon their condition and our need for them in light of current inventory. We reserve the right to reject any book. We accept only books that are clean, complete and in good condition. For best service please bring no more than one large grocery bag or box full at a time. Larger quantitities taken by appointment only.

If you think your books will be worth more credit than will be useful to you, please ask if there are any for which we can pay cash. Please note that once taken, credit may <u>not</u> ever be converted to cash. Paperbacks Plus credit slips are accepted at all three Paperbacks Plus locations in Texas -- in Mesquite, Dallas and Austin.

PRICE LIST

<u>New Books</u>: 10% - 20% off publisher's price.

<u>Used paperbacks & comics</u>: 50% of publisher's price or 25¢ minimum.

Used Hardbacks & Records: Priced as marked.

Magazines: See list posted in store.